Abou

Jen Parker is a book publisher in the Midlands helping authors to self-publish beautiful books with her editing, design and publishing services. She founded Fuzzy Flamingo in September 2017.

She lives with her husband Aaron, their two daughters and their shug Doug. Her aim with this book is to raise awareness for her chronic illnesses and disability, inspire people to seize the moment and travel more (when it is safe to do so).

Jen Parker

UNFLIP

Changing your life after
a life-changing diagnosis

To my wonderful mum, for always inspiring me.

Contents

Introduction

"There is no cure." With just four words, my stomach lurched as my world flipped upside down.

I left the rheumatologist's office in a bit of a daze. I had just been diagnosed with two chronic illnesses and told that there was no cure, I'd have it for life, and that they would just have to try and manage it. There was no escaping it, this was a life-changing diagnosis. Would I end up disabled? Would I be able to do everything I had set my heart on, including my career and family goals? Would I be able to live a normal, happy life? A million questions were running through my head, not least the first: would I be able to finish my round-the-world trip?

The first person I called was my mum. She was always the first person I told big news. She was my shoulder to cry on when I needed it, as well as my biggest cheerleader when amazing things happened. This particular phone call was from the other side of the world, and all I wanted was for her to hug me and tell me everything would be okay. I felt so far away. I could hear that she was worried about my diagnosis, so my natural instinct was to play it down and tell her I'd be fine. Why do I do this? Everything was certainly not fine, but I didn't want her to worry. I had so much running through my mind, and I just needed time to process it all.

For a long time, I shied away from telling many people what I was going through. I couldn't stand the tilted head look of sympathy as I felt like people would treat me differently if they knew I had a chronic illness. There was also an element of shame and embarrassment, as I had to combat questions such as, 'Aren't you a bit young for arthritis?' I'd go through phases of "why me?" and wonder if I'd done anything to cause this to happen to me. I'd also go through phases of "I'm not letting this stupid illness hold me back, I can do whatever I want to do!" Trying to find a reason or an explanation for my diagnosis has never been particularly helpful, but then neither has trying to ignore it and behave like I'm perfectly healthy, either. It's taken a while to get there, but I am finally finding that acknowledging my chronic illness, accepting it and finding ways to do what I want to do without causing myself more harm than good provides me with a great balance in my life. I don't always get it right, but I learn from my mistakes (not always the first time!) and I would love to share this with you.

Whether you have a chronic illness, or you are curious about what it is like to have one, come with me as I reveal the full story of my diagnosis for the first time, as well as hints and tips for coping with life-changing events.

PART ONE

Why am I so weak?

CHAPTER ONE

Growing Pains

I was often called a geek (or variations of that) at school. It baffles me now that it was often used as an insult, and I would often take offence, when it is actually a compliment! But kids can be cruel, and my self-esteem wasn't the best growing up. It didn't help that my academic gifts sometimes set me apart, as at the time I really didn't like attention to be on me. In year six, my final year in primary school, I was the only one in my class working on maths books from secondary school because I had completed the ones aimed at my own age. We were seated in the class according to the books we were working on, so I was made to sit at a table on my own! In my first and second years at secondary school I was getting good marks across my subjects and was made to feel like this was a bad thing by my peers, so in my second year I decided to stop trying. I didn't want to feel different, I didn't want to stand out, so I just started doing the bare minimum to get by. My grades came down to fit more within the average of the class and I was much happier. But now I wonder what may have happened if I had ignored the name-calling and my dislike of standing out, and had just gone for it? I may well have averaged out during those years anyway, or I may have become a genius! Either way, hindsight is a wonderful thing, and it has given me the tools to thicken my skin and go for what I want to achieve regardless of the fear of what other people think.

During those years, I was also having difficulties with my health. I'd always been an active kid, never particularly excelling at sport but thoroughly enjoying it, and I was a good team player. But during gymnastics classes (where I was happily distinctly average!), I started to get less flexible, despite practising more. It came to a head in year six when I tried to do a leapfrog, which I'd been able to do just the week before, but was no longer able to stretch my hips wide enough to jump over another person. I collided with them, and we ended up in a heap on the floor, with me clutching my hips, feeling like an old lady. It also just so happened to be in an assembly in front of the whole school, so I was mortified! I was just ten years old.

My mum took me to the GP and we were told it was nothing to worry about, just growing pains. Over the next few months and years, my hip pain and stiffness got worse, and my knees started having trouble too. Often when I walked, my joints clicked, particularly my hips, and you could even feel them clicking if you put your hand on my hip as I moved. My mum took me back to the GP numerous times, I had blood tests, was referred to physio, but the general diagnosis from the GP was that it was my age. Eventually, I had an X-ray of my legs and it showed that my bones were twisted, with my thigh bones twisting in so that my knees were closer together, and the lower bones twisted again. We were told that I'd grown too quickly for my muscles to keep up with the bone growth, so it had shortened and tightened the muscles, with the twisting exacerbating that, hence the pain and pressure on my hips. I was in my third year at secondary school when I was told that the only way to fix it was surgery, which would involve multiple operations, being in plaster from over my hip to my toes each time for months, with no guarantee that anything would improve. My mum and I even went as far as to talk to the school about it to see how it would affect my schooling, but we were both in agreement that the disruption to my education and the risks involved were too much to pursue. So, we dropped it. From that point, I stopped talking to the GP when I had joint pain, as it seemed a fruitless task.

I also had other health issues. I would regularly get poorly, a couple of times pretty seriously. One of those incidents was when I had a virus that wiped me off my feet. My mum came to my room to check on me and found I'd developed a rash all over my body. Fearing meningitis, the emergency doctor was called but I was put on hefty antihistamines because my body was having an allergic reaction to the virus. Although I was around twelve or thirteen at the time, I don't really remember much about that time because my temperature was spiking a lot! All I remember is the relief on my mum's face when I started to feel better.

When I was sixteen, I got a job working in a greasy spoon café. I was working with a couple of other girls, alongside the owner who did all the cooking. The kitchen was a small galley kitchen, which could only fit two of us next to each other if we both turned sideways! That made doing the dishwasher tricky. It was such a busy café that the dishwasher needed emptying by lifting the whole tray out and putting it on top of the dishwasher, then inserting an empty tray so that it could be washing the dirties whilst the cleans were dried and put away. I quickly found that my back hurt a lot while doing this lifting and bending, and I didn't know why I struggled so much more than the other girls. I also found it difficult to carry the required number of plates at once. The full English breakfasts were the most popular menu item and served on big oval plates. To serve, we had to hold two on one arm (there is a knack with the wrist) and one in the other hand, so we could carry three at a time, often up the spiral staircase to the upper floor. I felt like I was close to dropping plates numerous times because my wrist and fingers hurt so much carrying the plates in this way, and I felt so weak, particularly because the other girls were smaller than me and seemed to be fine. Why was I finding it so much harder? I only lasted four months because my boss, my mum and I all agreed it wasn't the job for me!

From an early age, I had my career path all mapped out to become a detective in the police. My brother and I played with our detective kits (complete with fingerprint powder and magnifying glass, I used to don my dad's trilby and crawl around in my investigations), I immersed myself in crime-fighting books and even had 'PC Pinkerton' as my invisible friend at the age of four! Despite coasting too much during secondary school, I got good GCSE and A Level results, and was preparing to continue my master plan at university. I knew I needed a good degree to stand a good chance of getting into the police, but it didn't matter too much what it was. My mum advised me to do what I enjoyed the most, as she always said people do better when they're enjoying what they do. I chose English Language and Linguistics, as I loved learning about how and why we use language in the way that we do. I loved reading but felt that books got torn to shreds too much with literature, and always leaned more towards the science of language. I applied to several universities, but the only one I really wanted to go to was York. I'd loved the open day, the people I'd met, and the course sounded absolutely perfect. I still have no idea what I'd have done if I hadn't have got in, so it's a good job I did!

University was the first time I'd lived away from home. The couple of years before I'd left had been amazing at home, just me and my mum when my brother was on his year abroad (my mum and dad had separated years before), and I was nervous about going it alone. But I loved the freedom, I loved the friends I made and I loved my course. During my Batchelor's, we did a taster lecture in 'forensic linguistics'. I was hooked! It delved more into the science of language, and was used to help catch criminals through speaker comparison (comparing speech samples from criminal cases with suspects from their police interviews to determine how likely they are to be the same person) and other methods. That one lecture led me to extending my course to four years by doing an extra year for an MSc in the subject. I got a temporary placement at the top lab in the country (and worked my way out of it too early by working too quickly!) and my tutor and I joked that I was going to revolutionise the police processes from the inside out!

During every holiday from university, I went back to my job behind the bar in my local pub, where I'd worked since the age of seventeen. I loved it there. I went from being the wallflower who blushed every time someone asked me for a drink to being the life and soul of the party, giving as good as I got with the locals' banter and earning decent tips. Village pubs are truly eye-opening, and the stories from my time there could fill a whole book! I also learnt that I physically had my limits. During the holidays I would often work seven days a week – split shifts every day except Sunday, which would be one longer shift. By Friday I'd be using every quiet moment to crouch down next to the fridges on the floor, lifting the back of my top to lean my back against the doors to cool it down. It would be on fire! My feet suffered too, and I needed to invest in orthopaedic shoes. But I didn't do anything about it. I never went to the GP, assuming they would blame it on growing pains or being on my feet too much. I also assumed everyone suffers from a bad back; just look at the number of adverts for back pain relief on daytime telly. It was only ever temporary, so I just gritted my teeth and pushed through until it was time to return to university.

Towards the end of my Master's, I was having difficulty with the fingers on my right hand. Up until this point, I'd still been having the ongoing issues with my hips, but was able to stay active, and was happily running 5k three times a week throughout the summer I was writing my dissertation. But my fingers were becoming a problem. The thumb and fourth finger to be precise. They kept swelling up and getting stiff and painful. I had been writing a lot of notes the past few years of higher education, as well as typing prolifically whilst writing my dissertation, so I put it down to being a repetitive strain injury because of that and persevered. The swelling would go down, I'd forget about it for a while and go on as I was. The dissertation writing was only temporary, after all, so I assumed I just needed to grin and bear it for a while.

I handed in my dissertation and moved back home with my boyfriend in tow. We'd met in the first week of our final year at university, the year I'd declared I was "steering clear of men to focus on my studies and then enjoy my gap year with my bestie". Great timing! He lived in Norwich and I lived in Leicestershire, so my mum invited him to come and live with us while we saved up to go travelling with my best friend Jo and his best friend Adam a few months later. And so, the planning began!

My gap year had always been part of my master plan: I would go to university, have my gap year travelling round the world, thus increasing my life experience, join the police on my return and work my way up to becoming a detective and solving crimes. I hadn't thought about it going any other way, that was all I wanted to do. Little did I know that my dreams would come to an end before they even started! But don't worry, there is a happy ending. Sometimes in life the path you are on comes to an abrupt end; there's a brick wall where there shouldn't be, or it simply drops off a cliff. You can't continue, so you have two options: stop dead and curl up in a ball, not going anywhere; or turn around and find a different direction.

CHAPTER TWO

On the Right Path

J o, Aaron, Adam and I got together and planned our
route, then worked out how much spending money we
would need to fund our way around: accommodation,
food, activities and treats. We all think with our stomachs,
so a lot of the destinations were chosen based on food we
love. Thai green curry, for example, meant Thailand was
an essential stop. We started out in South-East Asia, then
to Australasia, the Pacific and finished in the USA. We had
all worked long enough to provide the funds (with plans
to top this up during our longer stay in Australia with our
working holiday visas) and planned to travel for a year. Jo
fell in love not long before we left and so she changed her
flights from Australia onwards to speed up the second half
of her travels, so we knew we'd have to make the most of
South-East Asia with her.

In between university and leaving for travelling, Aaron
and I were living with my mum to save money. Temporary
full-time jobs were a bit tricky to come by. I got a job as
a receptionist in the mornings at a place called Church

House, which was the head office for the Diocese of Leicester. My mum thought this was amusing seeing as I was raised Catholic and was now working for the Church of England. It's all much of a muchness to me, though, and I had a wonderful welcome to the role. It was only a part-time position on weekday mornings. This was because the other receptionist was not able to work early in the morning because she had severe rheumatoid arthritis. She was incredibly stiff in the mornings and had much more pain earlier in the day and so needed the mornings to 'warm up', so to speak. I remember thinking how awful that must be. Having experienced joint pain myself a lot growing up, I'd had physiotherapy and hydrotherapy for the issues. The therapy helped but didn't make the issues go away. I couldn't imagine how bad it must be to have to change your whole lifestyle to accommodate that.

I loved my role as receptionist, but I wasn't earning enough money with the limited hours and so was looking for a full-time role. When I was offered one and tried to hand in my resignation, my boss told me to hang fire! It was totally unexpected, but they didn't want to lose me and so brought forward the date when they'd expected to require someone as a part-time PA. And so it was that I became a PA in the afternoons to the Head of the Cathedral Square Project, Pete Hobson. The project was brilliant as it planned to open up the area in front of the Cathedral to become like an Italian-style piazza. Ten years on and it looks fantastic now! The project had purchased the old grammar school next door to Church House. As well as the usual administration involved in this type of role, I had interesting tasks such as looking after the public car park we ran from the old grammar school (which is now the new head office, called St Martin's House) and arranging the sale of the random items left by the school, such as whiteboards. However, I repeatedly was hampered by illness. I had multiple throat infections that meant I'd lose my voice, which had never happened before, and wasn't ideal for a job involving answering the phones. I was finally diagnosed with glandular fever, which explained a lot. During that month (November 2008, three months before our travels), I also broke my fourth toe on my left foot. I was rushing around getting ready to go out with Aaron for our anniversary dinner and caught it on the corner of the wall. It was X-rayed and they found it was a straightforward break, so should have healed itself pretty quickly with no intervention. But it was still swollen when we were preparing to leave for our travels! I was looking forward to recharging my batteries on a few beaches in the hopes of a full recovery from my illness and injuries! I had the loveliest send-off from Church House when I left for my adventures, and I will forever be grateful for the wonderful introduction to full-time work I had there.

Packing for a year away is problematic. I had bought a large backpack, which was supposed to be lightweight and had the best support I could find for my back, which was still regularly sore if I overdid things. I packed as lightly as I could, my lightweight sleeping bag strapping to the bottom of my bag, my clothing limited to strappy tops, shorts, underwear, one pair of light trousers, my pack-away raincoat and a few bikinis. I was to wear my hoodie and trainers and have my flip flops in my bag. I took minimal make up and toiletries and the smallest handbag in the world for nights out, along with a couple of dressier tops for such occasions. All in all, I couldn't have taken much less and yet I really struggled to pick up my bag. I had to have help getting it on my back and was a bit worried about how I'd cope. I felt like a weakling when Jo didn't appear to have any trouble carrying hers, which was a similar weight, while she is a lot smaller than me. Why was I struggling so much? I brushed it aside and thought that I was just unfit thanks to my inactivity whilst poorly and injured, and it'd get easier as I went as I'd build up the necessary muscles to carry my bag.

I spent the evening before the flight at my uncle Ian's house, who lived fairly close to Heathrow, helping me relax. I have a crippling fear of flying and so was armed with diazepam from my GP, along with a warning not to drink with them or I'd be carried off the plane. I'd decided to only use them if I really had to, instead choosing a couple of glasses of wine that night. It was good to unwind and not have to worry about traffic trying to get to the airport from home in the morning. Unfortunately, Jo got stuck in said traffic and so was late getting there. We had access to the club class lounge, with free food and drink before the flight, as an apology from the company we'd first tried to book with for messing up our booking, so we were itching to get going! We said our fond farewells to our families and rushed off as soon as she got there. We ended up with only an hour in the lounge, but I still managed to squeeze in two glasses of champagne, a bucket-sized glass of strawberry daiquiri and a fresh fruit salad. I'd chosen alcohol instead of the tablets, and it worked a treat!

It was Adam's first time on a plane and the rest of us had only done short-haul flights before this, so it was a new experience for all of us to embark on a twelve-hour flight. The interior of the plane was so huge, and the fact we boarded from a corridor and didn't have to go outside or climb a rickety staircase all combined to help me relax, as I didn't feel like I was on a plane at all! We got upgraded to emergency exit seats because we were the only ones flying economy (premium economy was full, even though there didn't seem to be much difference between our seats), so the boys, both of whom are over six foot five, were very pleased to have the extra leg room. It was a comfortable flight, despite not getting much sleep, and it was a great start to our trip.

CHAPTER THREE

South-East Asia

Hong Kong: 02/03/2009

Our first destination was Hong Kong, where we were staying for two weeks. In hindsight, this was too long, and we could have condensed it to a week at the most, but it was good to have a gentle start to the travels where we didn't feel like we had to be doing something important every moment of every day.

We couldn't check into our hostel until the afternoon, but our flight arrived mid-morning, so we had a lot of time to kill. Close to the airport was the largest sitting Buddha in the world, so we decided to go and see it. This was via a very high cable car, so it was my second chance to face my fear of heights in two days. The first ten minutes were sheer terror, but for the half hour after that I got my nerves under control and actually enjoyed it. By the time we took the return journey I was a pro, even looking directly down at the highest points. The big Buddha itself was very impressive. I would have liked to do the walk right up to it to see the temple, but we had our huge backpacks with us and the jet lag draining everyone's energy meant we couldn't face it. I was relieved because I had been worried how I'd cope carrying my bag all that way, as my back and shoulders were already really hurting, but pride would have had me pushing through the pain if everyone else had wanted to do it. None of us had ever had jet lag before, we just didn't know what to expect, so it felt very strange to have no energy but not feel sleepy, to feel sick, yet strangely hungry. Even just eating lunch at the top of the hill felt like too much hard work, so we were all glad when it was time to check into the hostel. And so, our travels had begun.

Hong Kong was a heady mix of new smells (just walking down the street smelled different), tiny hostel rooms with beds too short for the boys and bathrooms so small you had to stand over the toilet (which had a waterproof cover for the toilet roll) to have a shower, rats the size of guinea pigs scurrying through holes in the hostel corridors (needless to say, we blocked the gaps under our doors with towels every night), facing my fear of heights every day with the towering skyscrapers and harassment from the guys touting 'genuine copy watch, genuine copy handbags'! It was sensory overload a lot of the time and could feel very claustrophobic. Luckily there was plenty of opportunity to escape the hustle and bustle.

Among my favourite trips were the zoo and botanical gardens (such a tranquil atmosphere in the middle of a busy city, it was magical), museums and art galleries when it rained, and stunning beaches. Pounding the streets made my feet hurt, particularly the fourth toe on my left foot that I had broken a few months before we left. It still didn't seem to be healed properly. And my back was getting very painful, which I blamed on the uncomfortable beds and all the walking we were doing, with hills particularly hurting me. So, it was always nice to relax and escape.

The funicular railway was good, but it was a trying day for me. The railway itself was incredibly steep, as all funicular railways are, and we could feel the pressure on us as we were pushed back into our tiny wooden seats. I didn't understand why I seemed to find this so much more painful than the others, though. It felt like my back was getting bruised from it. There was some very interesting-looking accommodation that we passed, and I couldn't help but wonder whether the inhabitants had one leg longer than the other like alpine mountain goats. We got fantastic views of the city and the islands from the top of one of the tallest hills in Hong Kong and got great photos. At the top of the hill was a building, which housed shops and a viewing platform on the roof. Sadly, I only managed to get two thirds of the way up the sky tower at the top before having the biggest panic attack I'd had in years. Having felt like I'd conquered my fear of heights in the few days leading up to it, I had got complacent and not taken any of my calming tablets. The escalators that take you to the top zig-zagged up the glass window that was the side of the building and so the further up you go, the further down you can see. Not only can you see right down to the bottom floor of the building, but the further you go up, the further down the hill you can see. This was too much for me, but luckily Jo, who is extremely good at calming me down, whisked me back down and settled me in the square outside in a matter of minutes. I had a lovely time people-watching in the square, and Jo was kind enough to take pictures for me from the top, so I still got to get a sense of the magnificent view. It seemed that although I had gone a long way in improving my fear, I still had a long way to go.

One of our favourite beaches on the mainland was Repulse Bay, which was only a short journey from the city and bizarrely smog free, clean and quiet. It was here that we got a taste of what it would be like to be famous. We found it strange that as we were lying on the beach in swimwear looking pink and sweaty because we just couldn't get used to the intense humidity, there were lots of Chinese people from a tour bus walking around with jeans and jumpers on, looking pretty chilly (probably from mainland China because it was even hotter and more humid there at the time). When the boys could no longer ease their rising body temperatures with a swim in the sea, they decided to go and get cold beers from the nearby shop the other side of a sand bank. Not long after they were out of view, we noticed a group of the Chinese tourists standing closer than they had been. We had known that they had been looking at us for a while, this had been a fairly common occurrence with us looking so different, particularly with the boys being so tall and me having very blonde hair at the time, but I had pointed out that they seemed to be taking photos of us. Then a small group took the opportunity of the boys leaving to approach Jo and me. A man started talking to us in Chinese. When we apologised for not being able to understand, he started pointing at his camera, then himself, then us. We understood that he wanted to have his photo taken with us and, when we reluctantly nodded, he called over a group of people. The next sequence is a bit of a blur because it all happened so quickly, but as they all took turns having their photos taken with us, with most of them doing the peace sign, more and more of them approached us until we must have had about forty photos taken. Jo and I felt pretty naked in our bikinis with all the fully clothed people, none of whom could speak a word of English except please and thank you (they were all pleasantly polite), but none of them touched us and they all seemed very happy. When the boys returned after only about twenty minutes, they looked incredibly confused and, when the people saw their height up close, they all wanted photos taken with all of us. It was surreal and we were all pretty relieved when they reluctantly returned to their tour bus. It seemed that they had not seen many pasty English people before, we were a novelty! We were very glad when the peace and quiet returned. I'd gained a new empathy for celebrities.

Lamma Island had the best beach. It was a short ferry ride from the main island and then it took fifteen minutes to walk to the beach from the ferry terminal. It was wonderfully isolated and even quieter than Repulse Bay. From there we did a fabulous fifty-minute hike to the best seafood restaurants in Hong Kong. It was a great walk, but it was surprisingly difficult and painful for me. I was fine on the flats, but the hills (and there were a lot) seemed to pose a big problem for me. The uphill stretches, which were long and plentiful, seemed to make my back and knees ache, while the downhill stretches were agony for my toe. I was getting very frustrated with myself, but the others were very supportive, and Aaron was a great help by letting me lean on him. Luckily, the food was absolutely worth it. There was a stretch of about half a dozen seafood restaurants on the sea front with a tiny harbour running alongside them. We chose a restaurant with a fabulous set menu that sounded too good to be true for the price. We were surrounded by huge tanks containing bizarre-looking fish and shellfish and we had a fantastic view of the jetties and tiny fishing boats from our table. It was also a great place to witness the spectacular sunset. The furniture was plastic garden furniture with paper tablecloths, so we didn't have high hopes for the food, particularly as it was so cheap. When we started to eat, however, we were pleasantly surprised; it was phenomenal. We had clams in black bean sauce, hot and spicy prawns, lobster to die for and perfectly cooked fish. It was so good that we returned for a second visit where I tried abalone for the first time. I had never heard of it before, but it is a delicacy in Asia. It came in half a shell that looked like an oyster's and the inside had beautiful petrol-coloured rainbow patterns on it. The abalone itself looked absolutely disgusting, like a cross between something that comes out of your nostril and brains. However, it had a lovely delicate flavour and tasted something like a mussel crossed with a scallop. We were very happy that we didn't have to do the mammoth walk back to the ferry after all that marvellous and filling food because there was another terminal on that side of the island. It would have been a very long journey home otherwise.

We met a couple of guys that were travelling Hong Kong together on our only big night out. One was from New Zealand and the other was English and we kept in contact. They were a lot of fun, and we had an amazing night, although it ended up a bit messy due it being ladies' night (free booze for Jo and me, which we shared with the boys in secret!) and we were all very worse for wear. Needless to say, after all that mixing and the copious quantity of alcohol, we were all pretty ill the next day and retreated to our beds. It was chucking it down with rain anyway and it was quite nice just to chill out, so it wasn't such a bad thing, although Jo and I could have done without taking it in turns to be sick all day (as I'm sure the boys could have done without hearing us!). It seems humidity and hangovers do not mix, and I would advise anyone drinking alcohol in a humid climate to drink more water than they think they need because it took me too long to learn that.

It had been a fantastic start to the trip. There was only one regret, which was that I would have loved to have walked up to the Big Buddha. It was too cloudy in the second week to return to do this as the views of the surroundings and the statue would have been severely impaired, so maybe if we stop there on the way to a faraway destination in the future, we'll return to do the trek.

Singapore: 11/03/2009

The journey to our second destination, Singapore, was terrible. Having had no sleep the night before leaving because of a child in the hostel room next to ours banging on the wall until the wee hours, plus a very early start, we were all exhausted. It was still raining, and flying through thunder clouds was unnerving, plus it was very hard to fight my phobia while feeling shattered. But we landed safely, got on the train at the airport and got to our hostel without a hitch. I also found an easier way to carry my bag, with the main bag on my back and the smaller detachable bag on my front, so it no longer felt like it was *totally* destroying my back because the weight was distributed more evenly. I still needed help getting it on and off, though. It was a very pleasant journey, except for the humidity. It was a lovely change of scenery not to be surrounded by skyscrapers and to see so much green everywhere and not just in the parks. As we stood on the train platform, we all took a deep breath and found it such a pleasant change not to be inhaling smog, but just smelling neutral cleanliness. The hostel was a lot more basic as there was no fridge or even plug sockets. It was literally just beds, but they were two bunk beds, so it was nice to have a bed to myself. The bathroom was a shared one down the hall, but it was very clean, as the whole of Singapore seemed to be. It seemed that there were perks to such a strict regime and the illegality of such things as chewing gum (to the point that apparently you could be imprisoned for having an unopened packet on your person) seemed to be beneficial.

Highlights of our stay included the trip to the island of Sentosa on the cable car (I was getting used to them). We went for a paddle on one of the gorgeous beaches and the sea felt as warm as bathwater. In fact, it was warmer in the water than it was out of it, especially when it was raining.

But my favourite day in this country was our trip to the zoo. This is famous as one of the biggest in the world. From the word go, the zoo became my favourite in the whole world, marginally overtaking Jersey Zoo, which had held the top spot since I was very small. It is designed to feel like you are walking with nature and they have it spot on. There was no straining trying to take photos through glass or wire because there was very little. The security mostly comes from invisible electric fences and well-placed ditches. It is incredible. We did, I'm now ashamed to say, ride an elephant. I felt very sorry for it because it had all four of us plus the trainer on it, the poor thing. Now looking back, I see that we shouldn't ride elephants for fun like this, but at the time (thirteen years ago at the time of writing) we didn't think anything of it, other than it being an amazing experience, particularly because Singapore Zoo is so hot on conservation. I now look at those photos and shudder. I have since read that they've now stopped the practice, which is a relief.

My favourite enclosure was where you walk through a simulated rainforest and there were lots of animals that roam free there. There were hundreds of butterflies, lizards, very cute pygmy deer (the size of rabbits) that were very tame, and tortoises. When we went up onto the viewing platforms, we came face to face with lemurs. We kept getting butterflies land on us and they had a particular penchant for Aaron's crotch! The parrots kept flying straight at us and several times when we ducked, we could feel the wind against our faces as their wings beat past us. There were also dozens of flying fox bats that were incredible to watch in flight and were the biggest bats I had ever seen. All in all, it was an amazing place.

We stayed there until they threw us out, but we had paid for a special ticket so that we could go on the night safari. We had an hour and a half to get something to eat before watching the night shows. Then we got a tram round the night safari and were shown various nocturnal and semi-nocturnal animals, such as hyenas and lions, which looked scarily close. We ended up leaving at 11pm, having spent thirteen hours there, but it was one of the most enjoyable days that I have ever had. I would love to go back and see it again. However, with it being such a long day and most of it on our feet, I was absolutely shattered, my feet were swollen and sore and my back hurt. We all felt it the day after, but for me this lasted a few days.

Jo and I had read about swimming with dolphins at Dolphin Lagoon on the island of Sentosa and hoped to do it on one of our final days in Singapore. When we got up it was cloudy but, as the bus approached the beaches, it had cleared up and was lovely and sunny. We walked to the lagoon only to find out that the only time you can do it is 9.45am (we got there just before 11am) and there is not a session on Wednesdays anyway. It was also very expensive.

The entrance price to the lagoon, however, was not too bad and it included entry to the aquarium on the other side of the island, so we decided to sunbathe on the beach for a bit and catch the lunchtime dolphin show. Sunbathing was difficult as it was thirty degrees and extremely humid. Luckily, the sea was warm and inviting and it was fun to swim to the nearby islands, so we could stay relatively cool. The show itself was spectacular. The dolphins were the species called pink dolphin and they lived up to their name. Although they were only juvenile (the young start off grey), they had lots of pink on their bodies. Apparently, they turn completely pink all over when they reach maturity. They performed tricks like waving, balancing balls, jumping up and hitting balls with their tails and they showed off their amazing intelligence and agility. Then the presenter asked for two volunteers that didn't mind getting wet. Jo and I were still in our bikinis, so immediately put up our hands. A guy was chosen, and they then pointed at me; I was so excited. Although mortified that I had to hula-hoop in my bikini in front of hundreds of strangers while the dolphins outdid us behind, the next part where we got to go in the water with them more than made up for it. I was introduced to her and had to stroke her while she got to know me. I then had to stand there while she kissed me on the cheek, hug her and then let her kiss me on the lips! Unhygienic, I know, but it was incredible. Luckily travelling had already eased my phobia of germs, so I was fine. I also had to conduct her to make her whistle. Every time she did something right, I gave her a little fish. It was so amazing and a little overwhelming. I don't know why, but I was struggling to hold back the tears as I felt incredibly lucky. And the fact that she was pink... well, you can imagine my excitement. I bought one of the photos they took, and Adam had taken plenty more.

One evening, we went in search of the famous Raffles Hotel to have a Singapore Sling, which at the time was on several 'top fifty things to do before you die' lists. When we eventually found it, we were surprised to have to crunch our way across the floor of such a posh bar. This was because they provide bowls of shell-on peanuts, the shell of which you traditionally just throw on the floor once you have peeled them. Although I'm not a massive fan of the nuts, it had to be done for the novelty factor, except for Adam who is allergic to them and was horrified at the sea of death he had to make his way across to get to a table! The drink itself was gorgeous but was the most expensive drink I had ever had. It was even worse when we got the bill because the menu price does not include the 10% service charge or 7% taxes. It was evening robbery when we worked out that it cost about twelve pounds (it is even more now, as this was ten years ago). It was lovely, though, and something to cross off the bucket list.

Singapore have a series of 'merlions' to go and see, which are statues of lions with the tail of a fish. Jo and I went in search of the biggest merlion in Singapore one day when the boys just wanted to relax. We took an umbrella to shade ourselves from the sun, which did help, but did little to cool us in the unbearable humidity. Still, we had a pleasant walk in search of it, walking through strangely English-looking parks and looking at the great architecture. I particularly liked the funky theatre near the big wheel that looked like a hedgehog. After much searching, and eventually giving up and asking a local, we finally found where the merlion was supposed to be. It was covered in a blue tarpaulin as it was awaiting maintenance. Just typical. It was supposed to be spectacular because it spits water into the river, but we had to settle for the miniature one in front of it. We had planned to visit the botanical gardens in the late afternoon, but the heat and humidity had completely wiped us out, and I was in a lot of pain, so we retreated to the hostel before going for dinner with the boys.

We were very excited about this particular evening because we were going to have the Singapore chilli crab, the (perhaps unofficial) national dish. It certainly lived up to the reputation. We found it in a tiny little restaurant with plastic furniture, but the smell had enticed us in. The crab was served up on a massive plate for the four of us and, armed with nutcrackers and small forks, we set to work on it. It was absolutely worth the hard work getting into because the taste was divine and incredibly moreish. The sauce was not too spicy but had a pleasant kick. The only problem with it was the mess. The tablecloth looked as though it had witnessed a grisly murder, while my skirt and top were also casualties. My skirt was rescuable, but I'm afraid the mistake in wearing a white top was punished. Aaron threw some juice across the table at one stage, escaping any splashes himself, yet covering poor Jo. We laughed so hard it hurt! To walk off the great feast, we went for a stroll along the beautiful waterfront and across some of the many bridges. This was lovely and I fell in love with the city at night. The dinner had had a strange effect on us, though, and we just couldn't stop giggling and being silly. Jo and I dubbed it the 'crazy crabs' and this was one of the reasons we got matching tiny crab tattoos on our return to the UK to commemorate our travels!

Malaysia

Kuala Lumpur: 18/03/2009

It was an early start to catch the first train from Singapore station to Kuala Lumpur, which we had booked a couple of days earlier. There was a long journey ahead, but the six hours flew by because I just read and slept the entire way; it only felt like a couple of hours had gone by. For the same price as the cheapest hostels we'd been staying in during the first few weeks of our travels, we managed to book ourselves into a four-star hotel in KL. It was lovely to arrive at about 4pm and be able to go straight down to the swimming pool after consuming our free drinks and relishing in our upgraded (for no extra charge) rooms. As we were shattered, we decided to spend the next day making full use of the facilities: gym, pool, bar, etc. We had sumptuous buffet breakfasts every morning and fantastic curry in the local restaurants. All our meals were less than three pounds in Malaysia and they were very generous portions and delicious. The best was in a tiny restaurant near our hotel. It looked like an English greasy spoon with plastic furniture and two sides open onto the street. The smell, however, was phenomenal. When we went in, we got very strange looks from all the locals, but we were to experience that a lot in Kuala Lumpur. Jo and I were seriously overheating because we had covered ourselves from chin to toe in respect of the local culture, but it seemed to make no difference to the stares as if we were aliens. We drew the line at head coverings because of the heat and humidity, so there was just no way to conceal our pale skin and my blonde hair. The waiter told us to help ourselves from the buffet and that he would know what we had and price it up at the end. This was very suspicious, but we did as he asked, and we didn't seem to get overcharged. He showed us what the dishes were in very broken English, so it was pretty much potluck what we were putting on our plates, but luckily it was all incredibly tasty. I had a delicious potato and cauliflower curry that tasted much like aloo ghobi and what I thought was a lamb curry (but may have been goat), which was delicious.

We did a lot of walking, exploring the sights of the city. When we went to see the KL Tower, it was not pleasant to climb the copious number of steps leading to the top of the hill where the tower was. The pain in my feet and back was unreal and I felt incredibly unfit. But the tower was spectacular. We couldn't fathom how something that looked so narrow could be stable at such a great height. At the Lake Gardens, we looked up and realised that instead of squirrels, they seemed to have tiny monkeys in the trees, which was lovely. We hired a couple of pedalos when we got to the lake itself and paddled among the fountains. It was very pleasant, but extremely hard work and very hot. It seemed that the pedalos were geared wrong and we had to work a lot harder than we should have done. The mandatory life jackets did not help with the heat either. All in all, we found KL spectacular, but overwhelming.

Penang

We arrived at our next destination in the dark. The train took eight hours and then there was a long drive from the port to George Town where we were staying. Luckily the taxis were very cheap and had boots big enough for three of our backpacks, so we only had one on our laps. The taxi driver was a bit crazy. He loved football and talked in English at a speed that we found hard to keep up with. He had eight children, five of whom supported Manchester United and three supported Liverpool. He said it was not a very pleasant atmosphere after the 5-1 result to Liverpool a few days before. The hotel was lovely. It was very basic, but very clean and the staff were really helpful. In the morning, we got up to make the most of our one full day. We walked to the museum, which I found very interesting. It was good to learn about the mix of three main groups of people in Malaysia: Malay, Chinese and Indian (hence the amazing fusion of flavours in the cuisine). We learned all about how they live and exist with their cultures side by side and sometimes even merging. The whole section about the Malay weddings was interesting too: they have twelve days of celebrations. I also loved seeing the fantastic clothes that they wear for each day with fabulous fabrics of vibrant colours that are all emblazoned with sequins. Jo and I then set off on the cultural walk for which we had a mini guidebook. We saw all the main buildings like the Town Hall, City Hall and the Queen Victoria clock tower. We also saw a couple having wedding photos taken in the most exquisite outfits. They were electric blue and delicately decorated with gold stitching and beautiful sequins. It is impossible to describe exactly how amazing the colour was, and the photos do no justice to it at all. It was mesmerising. We also visited the Cornwally Fort, which showed how Penang was founded by English folk. We felt enlightened. The guidebook was basic, but it turned out to be handy and told us some very interesting information. We felt like we had got the most out of the historic town, despite only having one day to do so.

Midway through the night before our very early bus to Krabi (our first stop in Thailand), I was struck down with a nasty tummy bug and so did not get much sleep. Luckily, it had largely subsided before the long journey; especially fortunate because the majority of public toilets in Malaysia and Thailand are simply holes in the ground with a bucket of water to flush it. It is advisable to carry plenty of toilet roll or tissues because this is seldom present, as well as hand sanitiser because finding soap (and sometimes even finding running water) can be a luxury.

Thailand

Krabi: 22/03/2009

We had booked to travel to Thailand by bus after the initial boat ride in order to save money. The bus turned out to be a minibus, which was not very pleasant for a ten-hour journey over terrible roads with a crazy driver. Jo and I had to sit at the back and got a nasty jolt every time we went over the slightest bump, which made sleep incredibly difficult. Adam and Aaron sat at the front with their knees practically up near their ears and had to poke the driver to stop him falling asleep because he kept drifting onto the wrong side of the road. This was not an experience any of us cared to repeat.

Eventually we made it safe and sound. We got a taxi from Krabi Town to Ao Nong beach where we were staying. The hostel was absolutely gorgeous. We had a room for four and the decor was lovely. The beds were all joined together, which was a bit odd, but they were so spacious that there was no danger of encroaching on each other's space. The only issues the boys had was that all Thai beds were built to the length suitable for the average height of Thai people, which, like the Chinese, is significantly shorter than the English. But there was plenty of space for their feet to hang over the edge. The staff were again very helpful and gave us great tips on good restaurants and activities. We headed out for our first Thai curry. I had a red one and it was fantastic, but I had lost my appetite and struggled to finish it. It turned out that the reason for that was because I was coming down with another nasty tummy bug, the second of many to come. I wondered if there was something wrong with my immune system; perhaps I was still suffering from the effects of the glandular fever back in the UK, or maybe I just hadn't got over the first stomach bug properly. I spent the night getting up every half hour and the next day had to stay in bed while the others were on the gorgeous tropical paradise of a beach.

I was better again by the next day, though, so we had another beach day and booked a fishing trip for the day after. The beach was just how you imagine: palm trees, white sand, green sea. The water temperature was fabulous too. The next day, the hotel transfer took us down to the boat on the beach. By the time we had got to the first fishing spot, we needed to take a detour to the nearest island because Aaron had come down with my bug. The two men driving the boat didn't speak any English, so it was difficult to explain why he needed to stop, but eventually they realised what we meant. Alarmingly, instead of waiting for him, the men just drove off with the remaining three of us in the boat and we couldn't get them to turn back. They explained in sign language and broken English that we'd go back for him soon. So much for the English-speaking guide we'd been promised when booking. Aaron was left at the beach (for which he has never forgiven me!) and we spent the morning catching loads of fish; a couple were really quite big ones. It was lovely. Then we headed to back to the island and tried to eat our lunch while avoiding the evil biting monkeys. One had gone up to Aaron when he was on his own, gone through his stuff and even tried his sunglasses on while we were on the boat. He'd also seen them attack some Germans for their food, so we were extra wary.

We went for a snorkel after lunch. Sadly, the coral reef was almost all brown and dying, a combination of pollution and the after-effects of the tsunami a few years before, but we still saw quite a lot of fish. There were loads of sea cucumbers, so I was happy because they are another of my favourite animals. We then headed to the boat and Aaron felt a bit better, so he joined us for the afternoon fishing. We didn't catch as much as we did in the morning, but we still all got some. Most of them were pretty pink fish with rainbow fins. We had to be careful to hold their fins down while we got the hook out because they were incredibly sharp.

They let us keep a few of the fish, so Adam, Jo and I (Aaron was still quite ill and in bed) took them to a restaurant for them to grill for us. They charged 100 baht each for the labour and the trimmings. We were happy because this was only about two pounds (most of our meals cost between one and two pounds in Thailand) and it was totally worth it. We had the big one in a garlic and black pepper coating and the smaller ones in a Thai sweet chilli dressing (both grilled). It was, without a doubt, the best fish we had ever eaten. It tasted so much better that we had caught them ourselves, and that we didn't have to gut them or cook them!

The next day we chilled out in the morning after the nasty bugs had drained us of energy then Jo and I went for a traditional Thai massage. If you ever have the choice, always choose 'oil' massages. The traditional oil-less massage we had was the most brutal I have ever experienced, even to this day. It felt like he was beating me up and my back was in agony for days after he put all his weight on my spine. I felt like I needed another one to get over it. This was, however, a sign of things to come, and my confusion at Jo not finding it anywhere near as painful and actually finding it beneficial during the following days would be cleared within a few weeks. We went back to where we booked the fishing trip and complained that we hadn't had an English-speaking guide and it had caused problems with Aaron being abandoned. They were very apologetic about it and gave us vouchers for another trip. So that afternoon we booked a snorkelling trip. This took us to four islands the next day and was fantastic. I was very excited to see the beautiful angel and parrot fish. As I tried to get out of the water at one point, which I was finding really difficult to do every time (why was I so much weaker than my travelling companions?!), Aaron, Adam and a boy that worked on the trip thought it would be funny to throw chunks of bread at me. I had hundreds of fairly large fish flapping about and sucking me trying to eat it and it was horrible. They thought it was hilarious and so carried on bombarding me until I finally managed to get to the boat ladder and escape. Although I kept reapplying the sun cream, my bum ended up pretty burnt, which made sitting down on the wooden seats popular in Thailand pretty painful. We booked a ferry for the next day to Koh Phi Phi (pronounced Pee-Pee). Jo and I were very excited because this was the island where they filmed *The Beach*, a film we'd all enjoyed.

Koh Phi Phi: 25/03/2009

This island had only relatively recently become inhabited. We only had one full day, so we wanted to make the most of it. The afternoon we arrived, Jo, Adam and I went for an explore across the beaches near our hostel. We saw colonies of tiny crabs, which live in holes in the sand. They were fascinating to watch, and the black ones were funny because the males had one oversized red claw. They were a species of fiddler crab and spent their time balling up sand with the movement of their claws in small circular motions in front of them making them look like they were knitting. We also spotted some half-day trips that looked good. The next day we went to Long Beach on our island in the morning to snorkel. The snorkelling was not great there, but the beach was still heavenly. The sunset trip we'd booked for the afternoon took us to several really good snorkelling spots. The reefs were less damaged there, so we actually saw colour. The fish were the best we had seen too; they were absolutely spectacular. We also got the chance to kayak round one of the bays, which was great, and I was happy I was able to cope with doing this, even though I was still in a fair bit of pain. The last bay we went to was Maya Bay (where *The Beach* was filmed). When we were told how we'd get there I was a bit worried because my back, fingers and feet were hurting. The bay was too shallow for the boat to get to directly, so it parked up in deeper water and we had to swim to a cave that we had to squeeze through. There was then a short woodland walk to the beach. It was so strange to see the familiar sights from the film. The beach itself was beautiful. We spent most of the time in the shallow water, which was incredibly warm and soothed my aches and pains wonderfully. It was still surprising us how warm the sea was. Then we made the journey back to the boat to watch the amazing sunset and eat fried rice on the way back to our island with songs from the film, including one that we will forever associate with this time: Porcelain by Moby. It was one of the best days of my life up to that point.

That night we went to a Black Moon party. This happens every month to celebrate that there is no moon in the sky (they also celebrate the full moon, so it's really just an excuse for a party) and it was so much fun. We had a few drinks, watched a very talented singer-guitarist, watched impressive fire dancers, a limbo competition and then danced the night away. Sadly, we had to go home early because Aaron's and my tummies felt very dodgy. That night our bugs came back with a vengeance, but we managed to get them under control by the time we had to get the ferry the next day to Phuket (pronounced *poo-ket*). It really was not very pleasant, and I was getting really fed up with spending so much time in the bathroom. I was crossing everything that I was finally getting whatever it was out of my system.

Phuket: 29/03/2009

When we arrived in Phuket, we had to get a taxi to Karon beach where we were staying. The hotel was called Baan Suay and cost six pounds a night, the most expensive we stayed in during our travels through Thailand, but it was worth it because it was by far my favourite of the whole trip, even down to the towels in the shape of swans on the beds. It was owned by a Thai lady called Suporn and her English husband, Daniel, who were incredibly lovely and helpful. On the first night, I had the best Thai dish I ate in the whole of Thailand, called Pad Kha Gai. It was coconutty and tomatoey and was so very tasty. It was not spicy, which was good because my tummy was still pretty tender. The next morning, Jo, Aaron and I headed out for a walk to the beach while Adam was suffering with the nasty tummy bug. Jo had been pretty lucky in avoiding it. The sea was so clear and very refreshing even though it was warm. We paid for sunbeds because the sun was so hot you couldn't keep your feet on the sand long before they started overheating. It was a lovely day, though, and nice to relax. It was surreal to look up from sunbathing to see an elephant with a rider on the beach picking litter!

One day, we hired mopeds (yes, Mum and Dad, I know they are incredibly dangerous, but we had helmets and I came out the other side unharmed and very unwilling to ever do it again). This was the best way to explore and visit the few sights to see round Phuket because they were so widely spaced. We went to see the big Buddha on top of a steep hill (I really didn't feel like walking up another hill yet!), which was very impressive. We also went shopping in the mall at the right time because it started raining. We saw Phuket bay and Phuket town and finished up shopping in Patong, which is the nearest town to Karon. It was fun, but very hot and pretty scary at times. The boys had got separated from us quite early on and gone for a long drive. They had some interesting tales to tell of riding in the rain and coming across a herd of oxen-looking cattle blocking their way and making them very nervous until a van saved them by beeping its horn and scaring them away.

Visa Run: 31/03/2009

Whilst watching the Grand Prix during some down time in the hostel I had felt really ill because I was at the first stages of a nasty cold. Who gets a cold in weather like we had in Thailand?! Aaron also felt pretty ill because of the seemingly never-ending tummy bugs we had been plagued with, so we all chilled out in the hostel. The rooms were fabulous with TVs showing great films, the pool was a lovely temperature and there was a free pool table, so there was plenty to keep us entertained. We then went to go and sort out the problem with our visas at the immigration office in Phuket Town. We had been very thorough in our research and read in the travel books and double-checked on the Thai government's official website that UK visitors get thirty days free visa entry. However, at the border control when we crossed in the bus, they would only stamp us up until 2nd April (fifteen days). It turned out that, although it didn't tell us anywhere that we could find, the rules changed in the December to make the thirty-day visa only apply to those arriving by plane. Any other form of transport only gave fifteen days. This was more of an inconvenience than a catastrophe because it just meant that we were to lose a day by having to leave the country only to return the same day. The hotel again proved to be the best we had stayed in because the owner arranged for us to have a day trip that incorporated leaving and re-entering the country to renew our fifteen days. She even checked by calling her friend who works for immigration when we looked a bit sceptical that it was that easy. So, we booked it with her for a couple of days' time.

Suporn's friend who owns an elephant sanctuary came and picked us up to visit it. We went on a forty-five-minute trek through the jungle, which was amazing, although again I realise now it isn't ethical and I wouldn't do it again for that reason. Aaron looked as though he would throw up for the first five minutes, but when he got that under control, I think he had a good time too. Adam and Jo were on the elephant in front of us. We saw a small, green snake on a branch of a tree less than a metre away from us and I was happy to get a pretty good photo. The guide told us what was making the deafening noise in the trees we had been hearing all the time. He said it was beautiful turquoise beetles. They look so strange when they fly because they hold their bodies vertically, like they're standing up with their wings outstretched. This makes their body look like a crucifix. Having looked into it since, however, the noise was probably made by cicadas, but I'm not sure that's what we'd been seeing (they looked like the pictures I've seen of jewel beetles instead, so they may be different). The views from the viewpoint were incredible. You could see the sea and surrounding islands for miles, which was breathtaking.

When we got back it was cloudy, so we decided just to relax by the pool for the afternoon, especially because it was going to be a tiring day the next day. We had to be ready and on the bus by 6am and would get back at about 6pm. We were travelling to Burma by bus and boat. Daniel said that he had to do it frequently before he got married (when he was allowed to stay indefinitely) and that you only actually get twenty minutes to walk around in Burma, so we were prepared for a lot of travelling.

Being ready and outside the hostel for 6am was not a pleasant experience; in fact, it felt positively painful. Getting up at 5am in my early twenties felt just wrong. Back then, it was the time we'd more likely be stumbling in from a great night out, not getting up! Since having kids and my own business, though I feel differently towards that time (although it's still not easy to get up that early!). We didn't even get to see a good sunrise because it sneaked up behind the mountains. The minibus was late, of course; nothing is ever on time in Thailand. Then we set off via a couple of hotels to pick up other people in the same situation as us, just to make our journey even more comfortable by filling up the bus. Another day of eating rubbish and sleeping in odd positions followed, with the odd perilous toilet stop where you risked every disgusting disease you could think of by venturing into squatter toilets with no water, either in the hole or the taps. Thank goodness for alcohol wash and baby wipes. Jo had a massive scare when a man's face appeared under the door of her toilet and stared at her for a while not saying anything. From that point we took to taking it in turns to go to the loo so that one of us could be guarding the door at all times.

When we arrived at the port, we got chucked off the bus without being told what we were supposed to do. We headed to passport control where we had stickers put on us to identify who we were with. A rather large man also came and took our passports from us. I was extremely panicky at this and didn't want to hand it over, but he didn't speak English and just took it. I kept my eye on him and made sure we were on the same boat as him. We were herded down to the dock where the jetty consisted of hundreds of long-tail boats tethered loosely together. We had to try and make our way across these to get to our little boat at the back. We squeezed ourselves through a tiny window to get in while risking a soaking in stinky brown water if we failed. The seats were about half the size of normal ones, so it was a thoroughly uncomfortable crossing to Burma, especially for the boys. When we arrived, it was another perilous leap of faith to finally land our feet in a new country. We were herded off to a tiny room where the man gave the passports to a couple of uniformed blokes behind the desk. We had to listen carefully for our names whilst trying to fend off the locals who kept trying to give us things (they would later try and get money for this if we had taken it like a couple of people did), put things in our hands or generally try and chat up the girls. It was highly intimidating, and I have never before had a worse first impression of a country. We were desperate to get out of there. We were all given our passports back with new stamps for leaving Thailand and two marked a minute apart for arriving in and departing from Burma. How ridiculous! It makes no sense at all other than to waste our time and theirs and earn them a tiny bit of money. After everyone was sorted, we were given no time to even leave the jetty of the port. Instead, we were herded back on the boat and made the gruelling trek back to our lovely Thai hostel. I could safely say at the time that I would have been happy to never set foot in Burma ever again.

Scuba Diving: 03/04/2009

Jo and I were very excited to get up the morning we were to start our PADI course to become open water divers.

This had been arranged for us by Daniel, who had an English friend called Simon who would give us one-to-two training. Daniel said that he was the best person for the job, and he wasn't wrong. We started off having a bit of a theory lesson to get us to know the very basics. This hardly took any time at all and very soon we were in the water with our equipment on. The first time we went below the surface with the full breathing apparatus was so scary. It is such a weird sensation to breathe underwater that it takes a few seconds to get into a rhythm and be able to do it naturally and not panic. We did various exercises to get us used to being under the water such as trying to find neutral buoyancy using the air in our jackets and then just by controlling the air in our lungs. It turns out I'm pretty good at this (I don't know quite what this says about me!) and it was a lot of fun. The horrible activities then came, which we had to complete to be able to move onto the next stage, which was the sea dives. We had to be able to do things like throw our mouthpiece away and be able to find it, clear it and then continue breathing normally. The crucial thing is to constantly expel air because if you are deep and don't do this it could cause decompression sickness.

We also had to be able to rescue each other and use each other's second air supply. But, by far the worst was that we had to fill our masks with water and clear it by blowing through our noses with our heads tilted back. This then progressed to taking the mask fully off, putting it back on and clearing it. The problem was that I had the remnants of a nasty cold and panicked when I couldn't clear it. The reason you do it in a pool first is for times like this because I had to go to the surface and went too quickly if this was in deeper water. Simon was really good and calmed me down very quickly. I went and blew my nose and tried again. This time I cleared my mask, but at the same time I cleared my nose! It was so disgusting, and I felt sorry for Jo and Simon who had to see it because I had my eyes closed! Luckily, they both found it hilarious. It did occur to me that it was odd that I had had such an awful cold when I normally only got them in winter. But I was very run down from the tummy bugs, and hadn't felt like my immune system had fully recovered from the glandular fever before our travels, so put it down to that. In reality, there were more issues with my immune system than just being depleted, as I was to find out in the coming weeks.

The last component before heading to the sea was the written exam part of the training, which we passed with flying colours. The hardest part for me was the maths component where we had to work out using diagrams and graphs how long we could dive for and how often before the Nitrogen levels in our blood got too high. I'm not too bad at maths ordinarily, but I think the combination of having the remains of the cold and foggy head with the absence of learning for a few months made my brain struggle to cope! It eventually clicked, though, and I got the hang of it. Next up was a very nerve- and excitement-ridden night's sleep before our first open water dive the following day.

It was an early start, but we didn't have to worry about breakfast because this was provided on the boat. It was so good to have proper bacon for a change. We met Simon there and he gave us a private tour of the boat and briefed us on the day ahead, while the rest of the people on the boat had this downstairs. The boat was amazing. There was a massive lounge area below deck, a large dining area upstairs and a sun deck. The back of the boat below deck was where all the tanks and other equipment were hanging and there was a diving platform off the back with two showers. Jo and I were so nervous that we kept having to go to the loo and it was a bit difficult to eat. Then the time came to set up our equipment and it all became a scary reality. We were actually going to dive to ten metres for real and there was no turning back. We pulled on our wetsuits (with some difficulty for me because my fourth finger on my right hand was very swollen and painful, my thumb on that hand hurt, plus I'd got a friction burn on my thumb from getting the wetsuit on the day before) and got our ridiculously heavy equipment on. We did our buddy checks on each other to check we had everything done up properly, including weight belts and buoyancy jackets. Simon jumped in first and then it was our turn. We had to have one hand on our mask and air supply and the other on our weight belt and step in. Then we all swam off a little distance and began our descent by letting the air out of the jacket and breathing outwards. It was absolutely incredible; so different to just snorkelling because it feels as though you are actually part of this alien world. We saw scores of beautifully vibrant fish on the coral. One of the highlights of this first dive was when Simon beckoned us over to a concrete bell with holes in. On closer inspection there was a massive Moray eel coiled inside it with its beak-like mouth protruding from one of the holes. Simon was wiggling his fingers in front of it to get it to come out a little bit and, as it opened its mouth, it displayed some very intimidating gnashers. I couldn't believe how big it was, and this was apparently only a young one. The array of fish was breath-taking, and I was so happy to be experiencing it.

We had two dives that day and the journey back to port consisted of us talking about what we had seen non-stop until we got back. It had been an incredible day and we had learned so much. We even successfully did our exercises, such as clearing our masks, with no problems. My cold seemed to have finally gone. The food was really good too: English-style cooked breakfast, Thai curry for lunch and yummy pancakes in the afternoon. Simon was really impressed that we only used the same amount of air as him. He said this was very unusual because he's had years of training and practice to control the use of air and newbies normally use a lot more because they are more excited and nervous and breathe rapidly and deeply. I guess we were naturals! Because of this, he took us deeper than he normally takes people on their first dives and this was very exciting. I was saddened to learn that the reason the coral was mostly shades of brown and not vibrant colours was again a result of the tsunami. It brought home the extent of the damage it caused. It was really quite humbling that on our little shores back home we don't have to worry as much as they do in countries like Thailand; we don't need the signs to show the evacuation routes from our shores and we are incredibly fortunate.

During the dives, I'd felt amazing physically too. The weightless feeling took the pressure off all the joints that had been giving me so much grief for the past few months. My back, hip and knee pain disappeared, and even my swollen toe didn't give me any trouble. However, getting back onto the boat was an issue. Everyone else climbed the boat ladder with their equipment on, only stopping to take off their flippers. No one else seemed to have an issue, but every time I got to the ladder, I'd get two rungs up and not be able to go any further. My back would scream at me and I'd feel like I had completely run out of energy. Every time I got stuck, I felt myself lifting out of the water and would be plonked on deck by one of the Thai boys working on the boat. I was impressed with their strength because they were all smaller than me, but also a little crushed by that. I'd be so drained of energy I needed help to get the tanks and equipment off, as well as needing help to get my wetsuit off because my finger and thumb were so swollen and painful. I had to push it to the back of my mind and just try and focus on the amazing diving we were doing, but that small voice in the back kept asking *why am I so weak*?

The next day we did our final two dives. I was pretty blue because I was grieving. My mum had called me the night before to tell me that my beloved cat back home had died. He was very old, but I was still absolutely devastated that he'd died of a heart attack. It was upsetting, but I had to suck it up so as to enjoy the possibly once in a lifetime experience. We had to complete the hardest exercise, which was the ascent from ten metres without breathing apparatus. You have to constantly breathe out and ascend unbelievably slowly in order to avoid the bends (decompression sickness). We both managed this, although it was incredibly difficult. We were lucky enough to see an octopus on our first dive of the day. It was inside one of the concrete bells that litter the ocean floor and filled the inside like a deflating balloon. It was so weird. These bells are an experiment in creating artificial coral. They were sunk to encourage life to grow on them as a lot of coral had been destroyed in the tsunami. It had been quite a successful project, which was nice to see. We saw all sorts of bizarre life, including a flounder. This was so strange. Simon was hovering and pointing at a seemingly bare patch of sand at the bottom of the ocean. As we got closer, we could see two eyes together and Simon moved his finger near it so that we could see the flat body of it as it sped off. It really was a comical sight. I thought the starfish were beautiful. There were loads of them in vibrant pink, blue and purple colours. They were about a metre across and their legs were really rounded.

We went in search of the elephants on our final dive. These were sunk to create something interesting for divers to see. On our way, we went through some concrete frames (more artificial coral to encourage real coral growth). I caught my arm on the side of one of them and it really stung. I didn't realise until one of the guys on the boat that helped me get out of the water pointed out that my arm was bleeding quite a lot. Simon cleaned it up for me and doused it in iodine to prevent infection and it was fine, but I was glad it was our last dive, or I'd have been worried about attracting sharks. This was our deepest dive and we ended up a lot deeper than we should have been, but Simon took us because he believed we could. When doing the course, you are only allowed down to eighteen metres, but we went deeper than twenty! It was very exciting, although the visibility was terrible. It was a sandy bottom with no coral, and it was like swimming through brown fog. We saw these really cool things that looked like very straight twigs sticking out of the sand. When you moved your finger near them, they retracted at the speed of lightning and after a while slowly started emerging. It turned out that these were worms. After a while, Simon got us to ascend and at the surface revealed that he'd got completely lost and we didn't have time to get to the elephants. This was a little disappointing but turned out for the best because we saw some incredible sights on our way back to the boat. We saw puffer fish, which actually look really cute when they're deflated because their spines lie flat like a funky hairdo. We also saw a ray in the distance, which was apparently highly unusual for the area we were diving in. It was beautiful and seemed to swim like a bird flies. At one stage we turned and were confronted with a wall of barramundi. This was something else. There were hundreds of them all facing the same direction and they were huge. As we swam towards them, they all turned as one and swam the other way. It was utterly surreal.

So that was it. We were now officially qualified to dive with a buddy in the open sea. It was one of the best experiences of my whole life and I couldn't wait to get back in the water. I can see how diving becomes addictive if you have the disposable income. I was worried that it wasn't without its difficulties for me physically, though. In the water I felt brilliant because every aching part of my body was supported by the water. On dry land, though, it was a different story. The simple things were proving more and more difficult, and I was embarrassed that people had to help me a lot. I couldn't help but feel weak and, frankly, a little bit useless.

The Final Days of Phuket

While Jo and I had our last day of scuba diving, the boys went on a big game fishing trip. They arrived back with a blue-fin tuna for us each. If you've ever seen one of these fish, you would know they are massive, but they are also extremely dense. The lovely owners of our hostel set up the barbeque for us. Meanwhile, the boys set about gutting the fish. A lovely salad was whipped up and the fish was cooked. Sadly, it would have been better to fillet them because, in order to cook them through properly, they ended up pretty overdone. They still tasted good, but there was so much steak-like fish that we were dreaming about it for days after and had to give the seafood side of our diet a rest for a good while to get over the experience. Their trip sounded very exciting and I really want to give it a go, but sadly didn't get the chance. I don't think I would have coped physically anyway.

A couple of days later, Jo and I went on a boat trip that island-hopped and took us to Ko Tapu, or 'James Bond island' as it is otherwise known. This is where the Bond film was filmed where Ursula *Un*dress (as my mum affectionately called her) emerges from the sea in *that* white bikini. The boat trip itself was fantastic. It was on a speed boat (a new and very exciting experience for us both) and it made us not want to ever travel by any other means on the ocean ever again. It was so much fun, and I can't wait to be at the point where I can comfortably invest in one! One can dream, right?! Although I don't know how people look so glamourous on them when the wind whips your hair and the bumps shake your drinks out of your glass! One of the islands involved a perilous clamber up onto a rocky ledge in order to make the short trek through the rock face to see a breath-taking lagoon. It was not exactly easy to do in flip-flops with a toe that did not seem to have healed from the break six months before. Was I not giving it enough rest in order to heal? But it was well worth it.

James Bond Island was a bizarre experience. You get off the boat onto a beach absolutely loaded with tourists of every description, go past a rocky cave with plaques from Sean Connery and co. and a little market selling the tackiest gifts imaginable. Shell with googly eyes anyone? No? Why ever not?! I started to think that this was a bit of a trashy place we would not want to stay long on, but I was soon to eat my words. You see, at this point we hadn't actually come across the part of the tiny island that is in the film and I couldn't for the life of me remember what it actually looked like. Then we came out on the other side and were hit by it. The fabled shallow waters with the backdrop of a gorgeous rocky-walled bay enclosed a giant stone obelisk in front of it. Pictures from the scene from the film came flooding back and we were taken aback. The miniature but very frisky tour guide took our cameras and took incredibly cheesy photos of Jo and I standing with our hands out so that we appeared to be holding the rock. I loved them, though! If only I had had a white bikini, you'd never have got me away. There was also a little staircase precariously cut into the rock at the side of the bay that took us up to a fabulous viewing point.

The next day was the dreaded minibus journey. This took us to the ferry terminal, from which we took a ferry ride to Koh Samui. Aside from a girl behind me kicking my seat for the majority of the way, the journey was pleasant enough and we got there safely. We arrived on dry land completely unprepared to know how to get to Chaweng Beach where we were staying in Koh Samui and promptly got ripped off for a taxi, but it was worth it for the fact that we got there very quickly and arrived right at the door of our new digs. It was to be a great place.

Koh Samui: 06/04/2009

Chaweng Beach is definitely the drinkers' paradise on Koh Samui. The streets are lined with bars, clubs, restaurants and stalls. The cracked pavements are heaving with bronzed and pink tourists and locals trying to drum up business. Our hostel was off a side street, again lined with bars, next door to a club. It wasn't actually the club next door that disturbed us (until the weekend), but a karaoke bar across the way somewhere. It sounded like cats howling! We deliberately chose this area because this section of our trip was intended to be the party section. It was, after all, my birthday on the 9th of April, which handily coincided with the full moon, the best night to party in Thailand. Adam's cousin and her new husband were honeymooning at a fabulous resort that was not very far away from us. I had been suffering from yet another stomach bug on the trip over from Phuket and it was in full swing on the first day. Aaron wasn't too peachy either, so we stayed in and watched films on the laptop between trips to the bathroom. Meanwhile, Adam and Jo hired mopeds (three pounds for twenty-four hours – ridiculous!) and explored the area. Adam also went to congratulate his cousin because he had not been able to attend the wedding. They had a fantastic time and found a waterfall, which looked amazing and made me very resentful towards my pathetic internal workings.

The next day, I dragged my bum out of the hostel bathroom to head to the beach with Jo while Aaron explored with Adam on the mopeds (there was no way my stomach could handle the jiggling of the bumpy Thai roads). I began to feel a lot better by the end of the day and was starting to dread my birthday the next day a little less, while crossing my fingers that I'd be well enough to drink.

That night I even started to look forward to it because Jo and I went dress shopping at the market stalls. Although 99.8% of the dresses I liked would go nowhere near me because all the dresses were in one size only and obviously not catered to the bosomed market, I eventually found one (thanks to nice stretchy elastic) and was happy.

Jo's birthday present to me was a massage with oils (to try and avoid the agony of the first time) on the beach. This was absolutely lovely except for when it felt like she was crushing my back. I was to know later in the trip why it hurt so much, but at the time I thought it was all part of the 'no pain, no gain' theory. I loved having my legs and arms massaged and, surprisingly enough, I even liked having my feet (apart from the broken toe) done – they had a weird way of touching so that it didn't tickle, even though I'm possibly the most ticklish person on the planet. It was also very funny to see the boys being pampered (and getting slightly beaten up) by small Thai ladies. Some of their kids were doing something funny on the beach in front of the huts and my masseuse had a crazy laugh that made it hard to relax, although it was lovely to hear such amusement. But when she was gossiping with the other ladies it was pretty relaxing because it is such a sing-song language. They may have been cursing and bitching their heads off for all we knew, but I enjoyed it. I did pay for it for the next few days, though, because my back hurt a lot. Perhaps I was just not cut out for Thai massages.

Feeling slightly battered and bruised, with a strange floating sensation (little did I know that this wasn't normal),

we headed off to the restaurant strip to hit a restaurant
we had grown to really like. It was pretty anglicised, but
the boys were kept happy with footy on the TVs and my
tummy was happy with a break from spicy food. Adam's
present to me was a delicious steak and cheese sandwich.
After that, we headed back to the room. Aaron had revealed
his birthday surprise to me, which was to stay in the same
hotel as Adam's honeymooning cousin for two nights. I
couldn't believe it. I happily packed an overnight carrier bag
(keeping it classy!) and we all headed off to take advantage
of the posh facilities. The taxi pulled into a looming arched
gateway and we proceeded down a long drive reminiscent
of olde Englishe countrye manors(e). I was gobsmacked to
say the least. A huge fountain appeared with three man-
sized monkeys in what looked like armour in front of a
spectacularly ornate reception entrance. My knees were
shaking as we walked through the huge doorway and into
the magnificent hallway and I was suddenly very aware that
I was in scummy clothes carrying a carrier bag with my
stuff in (I thought it looked better than my huge grubby
rucksack and I stand by that decision). We were led by
the receptionist into a room at the side called the library,
which was something appropriate for a Sherlock Holmes
illustration, and had a little glass of pomegranate juice and
a weird stick of young coconut jelly wrapped in a leaf, of
which I was not a fan. When we were finally taken up to the
room it took my breath away. I have never been in a more
beautiful hotel room. On the right was glass panelling to
surround the bathroom and, when we walked in, a huge

room opened out in front of us. The king-size bed was mounted on a wooden platform. On the bed was a curious towel arrangement, which was even cuter than the swans at Baan Suay in Phuket. The bath towel was twisted into a monkey's body with the hand towel as its head. There were little touches of elegance everywhere and it all came together to make me not want to ever leave. The bathroom was big enough to house a family of four!

The bath was so long and deep I feared I would drown if I used it alone. The toiletries (shampoo, conditioner, bubble bath and moisturiser) were in stone bottles, which set me the challenge of using it all before we left, seeing as I couldn't steal them like normal. They all smelt divine and I was very excited. Back in the room, the glass doors at the far end opened up onto a balcony adorned with comfortable sofas and the view was over the pool. Ah, the pool. It was absolutely beautiful. There was an island with palm trees in the middle, sunbeds and trees surrounding it and monkey figurines and fountains around the edge. At the left-hand end there was a restaurant and a bar, which had a little bar that you could only reach in the water. At the other end it was an infinity pool, the water seeming to flow directly into the sea because it flowed over the edge and the beach was directly beyond it. There were also various spas and Jacuzzis dotted around the edge of the pool. It looked fabulous and I couldn't wait to get in and have a swim, so that is exactly what we did.

By the pool, we met Adam's cousin Becky and her lovely new hubby and had a swim. We then headed up to the room to get ready (I could have stayed in that bathroom for hours) and headed out as a six to the posh restaurant we had spotted near our hostel. I was so happy in my new frock that I didn't care that the stifling heat and humidity made my hair (that Jo had spent about half an hour straightening with fairly ineffective straighteners) look like a lion's mane within ten minutes. It also started pouring with rain, which always helps! The waiters took an age to bring our food, which meant that I already felt pretty merry on the Mai Thais and Singapore Slings that we'd been drinking by the time it eventually arrived. Even when it came, they had got the order wrong and were very reluctant to sort it out. It was our first experience of bad service in Thailand because the Thai people are so lovely, friendly and helpful. Here was a different matter, though. Proof that you don't always get what you pay for. The faces of the staff were like bulldogs chewing wasps and they were unfriendly, unhelpful and frankly awful. The whole process took so long that we missed the whole of the happy hour in another bar that we had been planning on attending. By the time the bill finally arrived, we were thoroughly ready to vacate the premises sharpish. When it transpired that nothing on the bill was ordered by us and it was about a sixth of the cost of our meal, we had a choice on our hands. Normally I would have flagged up the problem lest I be overcome with guilt, but the fact of the matter was that if we had done so, we would have been stuck there another hour while they tried to sort it out and they did not deserve our money anyway. So, we paid what the bill said with a tip to ease our consciences and left a lot happier than we otherwise would have done. It was such a shame about the service because it was such a gorgeous restaurant. It was outdoors (with tarpaulins for weather such as my birthday) and full of trees. All the furniture was roughly carved from the same wood and the tables were laid in a very upper-class manner. My food was nice – a light fried rice served in a carved-out pineapple – even though I couldn't eat all of it because my tummy was still iffy (I told the others I wouldn't be drinking much for this reason).

From there we chased happy hour along the strip to get cheap cocktails and, although I protested, I got bought shots and drinks all night and proceeded to get a little worse for wear to say the least. I wanted to go to the drag show, but there was no way I could have convinced the boys (although I know they would have loved it!), so we went to a bar we had been to a couple of times on the little road with our hostel on. The promo girls there always dressed as cowgirls with shots in their gun holsters. There was one girl in particular that loved me. Every time we went there, she dragged Jo and I up to dance, and this time she got the whole bar to sing to me twice and hugged me so tight I thought my eyes would pop out. She also liked to strike me on my arm and tell me I was funny at everything I said, regardless whether what I said was actually funny or not. She left bruises! We moved on to the club next door to our hostel for a boogie before we parted ways and Aaron and I got a taxi back to our lovely room.

The next morning, I was woken early with the familiar

sensation of needing to throw up. I spent the next couple of hours doing this before we dragged ourselves down to breakfast and then the pool because I wasn't going to waste the facilities. The one saving grace was that this time the sickness was self-inflicted, so I knew it would pass much quicker. I felt much better after some sugary cola and a swim, and we had an enjoyably lazy day of lounging by the pool and watching the world go by. The resort was beautiful: big gardens with pagodas draped in fabulous fabrics, filled with enormous cushions to lounge on and monkey statues, fountains and figurines everywhere. I loved the showers for the pool. They were down a little path and looked like a big wall of coconuts. You pulled on a lever and a waterfall gushed over the top of it; it was lovely! I also liked the spas around the edge of the pool, which were ledges of various shapes and different types of water jets sprouted from them. Luxury! That evening, we decided to make full use of our bedroom facilities. We had a lovely soak in the gigantic bath with the amazing aromas of the bubble bath filling the room. Although I don't normally like bars of soap because they dry out my skin (I had suffered with psoriasis, a dry skin condition, from the age of about ten), I fell in love with their lemongrass soap because it made my skin feel fantastic. They supplied us with a spare bar wrapped up, so we took that with us. They had also refilled all our little bottles, so I had another day to use them all up. After that, we dressed in the huge, fluffy robes and slippers they supplied and checked out the TV. The movie channels proved plentiful in their supply of good films we'd not seen.

We also indulged in room service for the first time in our lives. I was a little freaked out that, when I called reception, she answered, "Good evening Jennifer," especially as the room was booked under Aaron's name: how did she know it wasn't him?! I ordered a mini feast and, although it was very expensive for Thailand, it was still less than restaurant prices back in the UK. When the knock came on the door, I answered it and he said, "Would you like it on the bed?" and entered the room with a humungous tray balanced on his hand with sweat dripping off his face. He must have run to get there because it hadn't been very long at all since we'd ordered. So, there we were: fluffy dressing gowns and slippers, great flicks and great food, all in the comfort of a bed I was dreading having to leave at the end of our stay. That night's sleep was incredible! The next morning, we woke to a beautiful day and headed down to a fantastic breakfast. Masses of fruit of all kinds, lots of continental goodies and cooked stuff and a little lady that cooked your eggs in front of you how you liked them. Heaven! Then we had the very distressing task of having to leave. I was devastated that we couldn't live there forever, and I felt a little sad that we had to go back to staying in hostels. But thank you, Aaron, it was an amazing birthday present.

That day we just chilled out because we had another long journey to face the next day. We wanted to get a good night's sleep, but that was never going to happen with Thai New Year just around the corner. The clubs and pubs were in full swing into the early hours, but worse than that was the wailing coming from the karaoke place. We only managed to grab a couple of hours before we dragged ourselves up at the crack of dawn to get our complimentary taxi-bus to take us down to the ferry. Of course, being Thailand, the taxi was so late that we started to really panic that we would miss our boat. When he eventually turned up, he drove like a lot of Thai drivers do (like he was running from the law) and we got there with seconds to spare and a big jog ahead of us with our backpacks to get to the right terminal in time. We were stickered with a red sticker to indicate that we were going all the way to Bangkok. The little bloke that only came up to my shoulder enjoyed pressing the sticker onto my bosom a little too much for comfort. We then found our seats and that was it, we were on our way to our final stop in Thailand. It was sad that we had almost finished our South-East Asia jaunt because it had been a fantastic journey. I would miss the cries of "taxi, tuk-tuk" of the mainland and "taxi, taxi-boat" of the little islands. I'd miss the fabulous smells from the Asian cooking and the lovely, warm sea. But we still had Bangkok to see, where we were planning to do all our souvenir shopping and enjoy celebrating Thai New Year.

Bangkok: 13/04/2009

It was a little nerve-racking arriving in Bangkok late at night and seeing men with massive guns searching cars. We didn't know that wasn't normal. I woke up after a much-needed sleep to several text messages and missed calls from my mum and my dad, both asking if I was okay, and I instantly knew something must have happened. I texted them back to say we were fine and went to use the hostel internet to read the news on the BBC website as my dad had suggested. It sounded awful as a violent clash with protestors and the army had taken place very near to our hostel, the first since the political unrest at that time had started. The hostel was run by an old English man and there were a couple of British staff. They said not to worry and that Thai New Year would continue in the local streets even though the city centre was closed off. There was a seven o'clock curfew in place too. They said we were far enough away from the trouble, and that New Year is the most important festival of the year for Thai people. He said to be careful, to stay near the hostel, but most of all to have fun. What wise words.

So, we stuck around the pool, which was the size of a children's paddling pool, until the afternoon, as there was little else we were allowed to do due to lockdown. The bar lady poured water down each of our backs at some point, which was incredibly confusing. At that point, we hadn't known that it is customary to soak each other with water and throw flour on the three-day festival that is Thai New Year. The Scottish guy that checked us in on the first night came in soaking and covered in white with a few of his friends in the same state. He said we should join them, so we put a bit of money in a waterproof bag in our pockets and locked the rest of our valuables in the safe, then ventured out onto the streets. Nothing prepared me for what awaited us. It was the most fun party I have ever been to during the day. We went out armed with two-litre bottles of water and when we got to the end of our quiet little street onto the main road we saw people dancing to the drummers playing all along it, massive buckets manned by large ladies with hoses, and people having so much fun you simply forgot that this was supposed to be a troubled place. In fact, it transpired that there was a burning bus just a few streets away from where we were. A group of people turned around and, when they saw us, they started yelling, "Why are these people dry?! We have to change this!!" Immediately we were swarmed with people of several origins: Thai, Australian, English, American; all with one goal – to get us wet. Armed with bottles and buckets and water guns of every description, we were drenched within seconds and could then seek our revenge.

It still got even weirder. And messier! Thai people came around with small buckets of flour and water in varied colours and wiped our faces, saying, "Happy New Year!" in Thai and English. There was no maliciousness in any of it; just everyone out having a great time and not caring how wet they got. Nobody minded getting wet because everyone was prepared for it. Businessmen in suits either had suits in a waterproof bag or were covered head to toe in waterproofs. We paid a bucket lady twenty bahts (it was about fifty bahts to the pound while we were there) each for the privilege of filling up our weapons from her bucket for the whole day and stood on the corner to thoroughly drench every passer-by who did the same back. Every car and moped that went past was covered in water and flour. One car went past so covered in flour that the only part of the windows he could see out of was where his wipers moved the sludge out of the way! It was all good-natured, though. The moped drivers went up and down the street with guns and buckets drenching bystanders. The trucks had crazy numbers of passengers in the open-air trailers around a bucket. This was the most fun part because they would just empty buckets over you as they drove by. One guy threw a whole bucket of icy water and flour over me, so I looked like a snowman. However, it was a welcome relief from the heat.

Then something even stranger happened. A moped pulled up with two people on it. The lad on the back, who looked around twelve, had a block of ice the size of a five-year-old on his lap. He had to alternate the hand he was holding it with because his skin was sticking to it. I looked with wonder as he passed it to our bucket-lady who proceeded to put it in her bucket. Up until this point, the water had been heated up to bath temperature in the sun. But now it was so cold that I actually welcomed cooling down a little. When the sun had gone in, we got slightly chilly and so decided to call it a day. I went back to write a message on my blog to say that all was well and to put people's minds at rest with the owner's poodle sitting on my feet.

Once we'd cleaned up, we asked the hostel owner where we could go souvenir shopping because all of the local shops and restaurants were shut. We were before the curfew, so he called a taxi and asked the driver to take us to a market that should have been open. It was very intimidating driving through streets that were deserted apart from soldiers holding huge guns. When we got to the market it too was deserted, possibly because of New Year, but more likely because of the troubles, so we simply had to turn back and return to the hostel. Jo and I had had big plans to purchase the table runner sets, cushion covers, and other beautiful materials we'd seen on our journey through Thailand, and send them back home via boat (to keep the postage as low as possible), but it was sadly not meant to be. It's another good excuse to return to Thailand someday, though.

CHAPTER FOUR

Australia

We arrived in Perth on 16th April having left Bangkok on the 15th. We were up at 9am after a night of no sleep because we had no air conditioning, ridiculously hard beds with sweaty leather mattresses. The hostel was only two pounds a night, though, so we couldn't really complain. We then had to hang around the hostel because the New Year celebrations had been extended due to time missed during the riots. This meant that the water and flour carnage was even more intense than before, and we could not step outside the front door of the hostel because we would have had to spend the rest of the day and all night in wet, floury clothes. We booked our taxi to come extra early because we knew that the roads would be mad round us. We spent forty minutes in the taxi before ending up at the front door of the hostel again because we could not get through the copious numbers of trucks, cars and mopeds with buckets of water being hurled from them. Our taxi started out pink and then looked like a Victoria sponge cake by the time we got through the other direction to get on the Expressway. Needless to say, we were glad we left plenty of time as we were able to check in early and get good seats. Our flight had been merged with the one before. Thank goodness we checked the airline website the day before because otherwise we would have missed our flight. When we got on the plane, we realised that this must have been because even the two flights together left the plane half empty. It was good because we could all sit together and spread out when we needed to.

It was only a short flight and then we had three hours to kill in Singapore airport waiting for the transfer to Australia. What a lovely airport. There was so much entertainment to keep us occupied and the time went really quickly. Jo and I visited the surreal butterfly garden, which was beautiful even though the butterflies were mostly asleep. There was a waterfall and lots of plant life that made us forget we were in the middle of an airport terminal. The second flight was extremely turbulent, and we flew over the most amazing lightning storms. It was out of this world seeing the intense flashes every couple of seconds below us. The problem was that it meant we got no sleep on either flight. We landed at 4.30am in Thai time, which was 6.30am Perth time, and so we got to watch another sunrise. I had a quick phone call with my mum to let her stop worrying about us getting into trouble in Bangkok. We said goodbye to Jo as she was picked up by her cousin with whom she would be staying, and a handy shuttle service took the boys and me straight to our hostel door. Luckily, our room was available for us to check straight into. To avoid too much jetlag, we headed straight out to explore and didn't go to sleep. I'm still not entirely sure if this tactic actually works! Perth is a lovely place and reminded me in some parts of Leicester, some parts of London, with a sprinkling of other characteristics to make it a great place. It was also surprisingly small (it felt smaller than Leicester) and so easy to get around. Our hostel was one where we would have to share a dormitory with other people. This unsettled me a bit because I found it difficult to sleep in a room with other people. Needs must, though, and the accommodation was expensive, particularly compared to Thailand where we'd just come from, so we had to suck it up. The dorm had bunk beds and so Aaron took a bottom bunk and Adam and I had top bunks.

Sadly, I had to prioritise finding a doctor. My fourth finger had been swelling and getting increasingly painful throughout Thailand and then the final straw was when the thumb on the same hand started following suit. I couldn't even open a packet of crisps because it hurt so much and I could neither straighten my fingers fully or curl them into a fist because of the swelling. They were stuck in a curved position. I thought that I must have some kind of infection in them, but I couldn't find any puncture wounds where I thought I must have been bitten by something. The helpful staff at our new hostel told me to get a Medi-card, which allowed UK residents to get medical attention at discounted consultation fees. It took ages to find the place because I was given the wrong directions and the place was tiny and tucked away. I found it eventually and the card worked instantly, so I could book an appointment for the next morning.

The GP was brilliant, but it wasn't pleasant news. He told me straight away that he was almost certain what the problem was, saying, "I know what it is and you're not going to like it." I realised that he was right that I wouldn't like it when he said that he thought it might be rheumatoid arthritis. He explained what could be done and how, and sent me straight away to get blood tests. He also said to book another appointment with him when I was to get the results in only a couple of days' time. He told me that if it was confirmed, I would have to stay in Perth one month at the minimum and said it was more likely to be two. We had only intended to stay a couple of weeks because there wasn't much we had planned to do in and around Perth, so we decided to change our original plans and stay to work in Perth instead of working as we travelled across Australia, as had been the original plan. The boys were incredibly supportive and no amount of my insisting they should not let me ruin their travel plans and that they should continue without me would get rid of them! They decided it would be best to save money for the rest of the trip while we were in Perth and said that they started the trip with me and so would finish it with me. I felt very lucky to have such great friends. I had been referred to a rheumatology specialist on an urgent basis, so instead of having to wait the usual four weeks – which still would have been far faster than the NHS in the UK – I got to see him in five days. This was good news because the quicker I was to get started on medication, the less effect the illness would have in the short and long term and the sooner we could head out on our road trip across the south coast with detours across the MacDonnell range and Uluru (known to most Brits at the time as Ayers Rock). I didn't realise just how much our plans would have to change, though.

We met a couple of guys in our dorm room who were cool and the five of us went on a night out on our last night in that hostel. We drank boxes of wine and then went to a bar down the road. It was actually really good fun and nice not to feel so awful the day after, unlike drinking in the humidity of South-East Asia. Danny went on to the North West, but we met up again with Sami, the Fin, for another night out before he left for Thailand. We went to Cottesloe Beach on a Sunday night as we had read that it is traditional to watch the sunset in the beach-side bars with your favourite bevvie. Sadly, we slightly missed the sunset, but we still got some great pictures of the last of the red sun across the sea. It really was beautiful. Then we hit the booze rather gently due to the fact beers were a fiver a pint (expensive for us over a decade ago) and wine wasn't much less. Sami had thought ahead and brought a cool bag with some tinnies in. He was fitting in with the Aussie culture already! We had a great time in one of the beach bars, which was absolutely heaving with a mixture of locals and backpackers. We got a free train ride back to Perth because the ticket machine had eaten too much money, then we hit a pool hall down the road from our hostel. The final time we saw Sami was the day we spent on Cottesloe Beach.

This is in between Perth and Fremantle and we were told it was the best beach near Perth and they weren't far wrong. The sun was beating down and the waves were huge. I was wiped out twice while paddling, much to the amusement of Aaron, particularly when I lost my bikini! I was standing with my hands and arms covering my nether regions, my bikini top hanging down my back and the bottoms round my ankles! It was clear after that why the locals were wearing wetsuits in the water. It was so much fun, though. We said farewell and bon voyage to Sami and headed back to our new hostel: the infamous YMCA.

We had to stay in this hole of a place for a whole week and I couldn't wait to get out. The rooms were very basic and okay, if a little worn and pretty dusty. It was nice to have a double room and a separate single for Adam to have a little space. The toilets were down the hall and there was a common room with a TV. It felt a bit like university accommodation, but with junkies and smelly weirdos instead of students. It didn't help that there was no hob in the kitchen, so we either ate microwave food or salads because eating out was way out of our price range; Perth was more expensive than London. One morning I had to hold my bladder because the toilet seats were covered in excrement. I did wonder how that was even possible.

While we searched for a more long-term place to stay, we lived for a few days in the campervan we had just bought. We stayed in a campsite that was a lot more within budget, with a swimming pool so cold it took your breath away (the locals couldn't believe I swam in it every morning), but not practical for more than a few days. We found it hard to find somewhere to rent for less than six months. We had thought we'd only need it for a couple of months, but with hindsight it turned out we could have gone for the longer, cheaper six-month contracts. We found an apartment we could rent short-term just north of the city in a suburb called Tuart Hill – Tuart meaning tree. Pretty much the only criteria we had to fulfil for our landlady was that we were not Irish. It sounds strange, but she had strong prejudices against them because she had two separate groups of Irish tenants and they caused a lot of trouble. I tried to stick up for the general Irish population, but she was having none of it.

My job hunt on the internet was throwing up nothing on the temp job front, so I did it the good old-fashioned way of going into every bar, restaurant, shop and brothel (only kidding!) and saying the age-old words, "Gizza job!" I managed to pick up a few weekend waitressing shifts at the Italian restaurant down the road, but not many. We were struggling to find any particularly stable employment because the recession had hit almost as our plane landed. This would only change when they announced on the news that Australia was never officially in a recession because they only spent one month without economic growth and there needs to be more for that official term to be used. When that happened, the temp agency flood gates opened, and I had much better luck. One saving grace was that apparently the south and east coasts had been hit harder on the temporary job front, so we were actually better off changing our plans to work in Perth anyway. It's good to look for the silver linings, and my mum's belief that everything happens for a reason rang true in that instance.

It was very nice to have a proper fridge from which people didn't steal our food and a cooker so that we could eat properly again. Our campervan was also an absolute beauty. The first campervan we viewed was in Fremantle. This was a lovely city by the sea. The city beach was tiny, but very nice. There was a much bigger and better beach in North Fremantle, however. The architecture on the beach front made me feel like I was in a nautical Western. It was all white and blue with wooden saloon doors on the shops. I loved the atmosphere of backpackers and surfers. I would later be thrilled to get a job there. It turned out that it wasn't the van for us, though, because we found a bigger, better one. We needed a bit more space to accommodate the boys' taller than average height. She was beautiful, despite being even older than Elton, my beloved gold E-reg Nissan Micra back home. She was bright yellow with a graffiti-style picture of a woman with flowing hair down the side and went by the name of Sunny. We took her to visit my second cousin Tom and his wife Kim while they were in their city home. They also had a vineyard home near Mt Barker down south. They are lovely people. Tom reminded me very much of my uncle Ian (his cousin) and Kim is very funny. They put on a massive barbeque that could have fed thousands! At that point we were still in the YMCA and had been eating badly for ages, so we couldn't have been more grateful. The boys loved Tom because he plied them with beer and then brought out a 2004 bottle of Shiraz from his own vineyard. I had a tiny sip and it had an amazing burst of flavour. I was gutted I couldn't have more, but I had decided to drive as I was officially tee total. It was hard to believe for a lot of people, but the medication I was on required it. At least my liver was starting to forgive me for the beating it had taken during my teenage years and early twenties! On the way back from Tom's, we stopped off at King's Park. This offered amazing views of the city at night when it was all lit up and it did not disappoint. It was absolutely stunning.

PART TWO

Will I End Up in a Wheelchair?

CHAPTER FIVE

The Day My Life Changed Forever

The appointment with the rheumatologist came round very quickly. He talked to me about my own health history, as well as my family history. He asked me about my psoriasis, how long I'd had it and to what extent. He checked me out all over, including getting me to do various stretches like trying to touch my toes, and examined my nails on my fingers and toes. He asked me if I'd noticed my nails were ridged and I had, but hadn't thought anything of it. He then went on to explain that the swelling in my fingers and that toe that hadn't healed since the break, along with the psoriasis and ridged nails led him to believe I had psoriatic arthritis. He explained in very simple terms that my immune system was overactive and, instead of attacking things it should, such as bugs, it was attacking the linings of my peripheral joints. It was also causing the psoriasis because the immune system was telling my brain there was a problem with my skin when there wasn't, so new skin cells were being grown on top of existing skin cells, the layers were building up and then getting flaky, cracking and bleeding (when it was at its worst).

He also asked me about back pain. I explained about the issues I'd experienced with the waitressing job and then the bar work, but explained that it was normal. Everyone experienced back pain, right? Well, that was wrong! He said that mechanical back pain gets better when you rest, but as my pain and stiffness was usually worse in the mornings when getting up from sleeping, it was indicative of ankylosing spondylitis (now also known as axial spondyloarthritis or axial SpA), a disease similar to the psoriatic arthritis but affecting the spine and pelvis. My white blood cell count and inflammatory markers were sky high in my blood tests, so his first priority was getting the inflammation under control. He prescribed methotrexate for the psoriatic arthritis, an immunosuppressant in a group of drugs called disease-modifying anti-rheumatic drugs (DMARDs) used to treat psoriatic arthritis. He also prescribed anti-inflammatories and steroids to bring down the swelling because the methotrexate would take a while to become effective.

I left the rheumatologist's office in a bit of a daze. I had just been diagnosed with two diseases similar to rheumatoid arthritis called psoriatic arthritis and ankylosing spondylitis and told that there was no cure, I'd have it for life, and that they would just have to try and manage it. I thought about the receptionist from Church House who was severely disabled from rheumatoid arthritis. Would I end up like her? I was fit, healthy and active, would that come to an end? I wandered across the road to a nearby park and sat on a bench contemplating what my life might look like now with a life-changing diagnosis. I called my mum and had a cry about the diagnosis, whilst also trying to reassure her that I was fine, and she shouldn't worry! I am very much my mother's daughter sometimes, as she did the same with me whenever she had health challenges.

I had to have blood tests every two weeks when I was first on the methotrexate to monitor my liver because it can get damaged by it. One day, a man in front of me in the queue came out of the clinic room with a bottle in a plastic bag and sheepishly headed for the loo to squeeze out a sample. I think that they should have a secret passageway to the toilet from the clinic room because this is always embarrassing, particularly afterwards when you have to parade with your sample in the lovely clear plastic bag they provide, which only seems to magnify what you're holding. When the nurse called me in straight after, I was hoping either the bloke was quick at urinating or the nurse would take her time with the administrative stuff before taking my blood. I got neither wish as he knocked and entered the room at the exact moment that she was pushing the needle into my arm and she jumped. She then turned around and got distracted as she tried to sort his sample out while sampling me. I felt the needle wiggle and my heart sank. I knew she knew what was going to happen because, despite us having a joke about me making my residency at the clinic permanent because I was there so frequently, she gave me a leaflet for the first time outlining aftercare instructions to prevent bruising, which I found rather suspicious.

I was called in to work at the restaurant (the waitressing job) at the last minute and so the instruction to not carry anything in the arm from which the blood was taken went out of the window. The bruising showed before I started anyway, but the looks of people seeming to question whether I fit the stereotypical image of a junkie could just have been my paranoia. The next day, however, it had grown into a lovely black pattern with a yellow and red outline that resembled a footprint of a small duck that had trodden in wet paint. I arrived at work and my boss, Wasantha, asked if I had burned myself. There was no mistaking the looks on the punters' faces this time either as they caught sight of my arm every time I put a plate or drink down on the table. I had it checked out at the pharmacy to err on the side of caution and she explained that my lovely medication meant that I bruised more easily. That, combined with my tendency to bruise like a peach due to my pasty complexion, meant I was to look like a satellite view of Earth quite frequently from that point on. I was dreading anyone suggesting paintball!

CHAPTER SIX

Working Life, Australian Style

I got a little job working four hours a day, six days a week as a fundraiser. The perks were that I got to spend four hours a day in the fresh air, chat to lovely people and feel good that I was doing something for a good cause. The downsides were that I had to be on my feet for four hours a day, sometimes in horrible weather, be abused by mean people and feel guilty that I was getting money out of a good cause. But the temporary job market was very small thanks to the recession and beggars couldn't be choosers at that time. It didn't do my painful back, hips and feet any good, though. I thought to myself at least I wasn't selling anything or making people sign up for anything. I just knocked and they chose to give me a donation or not. There was no taking of details, no tying into long-term donating, just one-off donations.

I was still working at the restaurant too, much to my back's dismay. I fundraised 1.30pm-5.30pm, then waitressed 6.30pm until midnight. I was very happy to have the money coming in, but I couldn't last very long on that schedule. I worked forty-six hours the second week I worked as a fundraiser. In his absence of work, though, Aaron had become quite the house-husband and had my dinner waiting on the table for me on my return from my first job, so that I had time to get ready for the second. I had him very well trained for a short while. There were days, though, where I'd barely make it to the end of my waitressing shift, and I'd have to lie flat on the cool tiles of the living room floor when I got home, soothing my red-hot sore back and sobbing. The pain was unbearable at times. I'd also be exhausted, and there were several times I didn't have the energy to get up when I fell asleep on the sofa and Aaron would carry me to bed. Thankfully, our bedroom was next door to the living room, so it wasn't far to carry me, but that shows how exhausted I was. It wasn't until a few years down the line that I learnt that fatigue is a major part of the arthritis. It makes sense, really, when you think about how much my body was fighting itself, using up energy unnecessarily. I was constantly looking for a more suitable job and was happy when I managed to secure it. I had to eat my words about not having to sell anything, though!

The new job was in telesales, so I felt like I had sold my soul to the devil, but desperate times, as they say. The interview was pretty laid back where my boss told me what the job entailed, which was cold calling to set up leads for the sales department. He asked questions to determine whether I was okay with taking abuse. It was a gruelling journey to get there on public transport with a bus ride, a train ride and a second bus ride, taking an hour and a half. But surprisingly I was actually not too bad at it. One month I earned the company quite a bit of dough, but I never managed to hit my bonus. I got a retainer plus twenty dollars for each sale. The bonus would have been an extra hundred on top of that if I got five sales (where the telesales lead converted into a sale when the salesman visited in person) in one week, but the most I ever obtained was four. People got fired if they went too many days without a lead or if their leads never confirmed, which is the call made by the manager to make sure the customer would be there. Despite not getting many leads, I never got fired. This confused me because a couple of people with more leads than me did get fired, which was a lot of stress and pressure to be feeling every day. When I handed in my notice, I asked why I'd not been fired, for curiosity's sake, and he told me that, even though I didn't get many leads, the leads I did get were very likely to get sales because they were very strong.

The stress just wasn't worth it, though, and it had a really negative impact on all aspects of my health at an already taxing time. I got laryngitis four times in five weeks. One morning, I had to call the doctor as soon as I got up for work because I'd had scary chest pains all night on top of the palpitations I had been experiencing all week from the steroids (I was put on a five-day course of very high steroids for the flare-up I'd been experiencing) and I was running a temperature. It felt like someone was alternately stabbing and squeezing my heart. They fit me in straight away, so I threw my makeup bag in my bag and jumped on the bus with wet hair (still foolishly thinking I could go straight to work after my appointment because the doctor would miraculously give me my voice back). The manager phoned me while I was in the waiting room and said, "Ah… you don't sound much better." I said I would call him and let him know what the doctor said when I'd seen her and I went in. My ears were fine and my throat wasn't as red as she expected, but she was concerned about my chest. She sent me for an ECG to check there were no abnormal rhythms in my heart or clots in my lungs. It was all pretty scary, especially when the nurse ordered my clothes off and produced a piece of machinery that looked like Doctor Octopus from *Spiderman*! It didn't take very long and the results were fine, if a tad fast. So, the doctor came to the conclusion that it must just be a virus or infection in my chest and put me on antibiotics. I just had to watch that the pains didn't get worse and I didn't start puking blood. I was fine, though; the only concern at the time was my job, with its lack of security.

The day I started to lose my voice with laryngitis for the fourth time, I got a call from a temp agency offering me a job. I was so happy to go straight into the manager's office after my break and say, "I'm no use to you or me in this job and I hate it, so I'm handing in my notice." He asked if I could finish the day, which didn't make any sense to me because this gave me free reign to just chat to people all day and try not to get leads because I wouldn't have received the bonus if any of them sold! It was the best day I ever had there. I did make a few friends and we met up a couple of times after I left. They were Vanda, Scotty, Starky and Jodie and I thank them for keeping me sane in the few months I had to do the worst job I have ever done in my life!

By this point I knew that the original plan to stay in Perth only two weeks, plus the secondary plan to stay just a few months, were both out of the window. I was put on a new medication (the third type) and so was told at that time that I had to be monitored until at least October. The first and second medications only worked in conjunction with steroids, which I had to come off as soon as possible because they are only a short-term medication. They have serious side effects such as thinning of the skin and incredible weight gain (an Australian acquaintance commented on a night out that I had a 'flabby belly', which was true because I had put on over a stone, but still not nice to hear), as well as leaching vitamins like calcium from the body, so the sooner I could come off them the better. Over the space of the six months that I was on them, I put on a stone and a half, and most of that happened within the first four weeks. I was prescribed a new medication called Enbrel, which was a form of anti-TNF (tumour necrosis factor, a protein that's part of the immune response and causes inflammation). This group of drugs work by suppressing the immune system to reduce inflammation. I had to inject myself with it once a week. This was daunting at first, but was not as bad as I thought. Plus, I saw the effects after the first injection, so I was extremely happy. I was supposed to be in remission within three months if it was fully effective and then it would just be a matter of keeping me there.

In the meantime, Adam had found a landscape gardening job for a company in Huntingdale. The only problem was that he had to get up at around 5am, which was a huge shock to the system after the travelling lifestyle of late nights and lie-ins. Aaron got a job as a 'bussy' (a general dogsbody, who collects glasses, serves drinks, does heavy lifting and anything that other people don't want to do) in Burswood Casino. This was part of a massive complex in Perth that incorporated a variety of bars, a club and the casino. It was quite tough to get the job because first you needed to gain a license to be able to work in a bar in most states in Australia, get police clearance and have more training with the company. It was great that he was earning money, but strange not having a house-husband any more. He still had my dinner on the table when I got in from work when he wasn't working, though!

Some of the only recreational activities we regularly enjoyed during our employment months due to lack of time and funds were fishing and the cinema (on cheap Tuesdays when tickets were half price). Fishing was great fun. The boys found a spot where all they could catch were small puffer fish every ten seconds because they had a population boom in Scarborough. Aaron and I went to the South Mole (a brilliant name) in Fremantle. We both caught pretty fishies, but they were too small to eat. We were yet to catch dinner as we did in Thailand.

It was comical to return home to find Aaron sprawled on the couch after his first shift at Burswood moaning like mad. It was a teeny bit of a shock to the system after so long away from working life. It was a positive step, however, because it meant that at last we were all employed and able to start properly saving for the next leg of our travels that were scheduled to start in October.

★★★

During my stint as a telemarketer, I had to have a couple of weeks off when a couple of viruses effectively ran back-to-back. So, I had to find some entertainment to take my mind off the fact that I wasn't earning (no sick pay with the sales job) but still had rent and doctor's bills to pay. I went to the charity bookshop down the road and bought six books for five dollars. I had ploughed through several books that I had bought from there and so I stocked back up, including more books by my beloved Gerald Durrell who founded Jersey Zoo. It seemed there was a fellow fan of his locally, as there were always books of his popping up!

On my walk to the shops one day, I walked past a house with a tree outside absolutely laden with lemons. I saw the sign I'd seen a few times, saying, 'Please do not take the lemons', but there was an additional sign that had been recently put up. It said, 'Buy lemons 50c a kilo'. I stopped off at the little supermarket to pick up some tortilla chips and salsa because I'd taken some previously made chilli out of the freezer to make nachos. Out of curiosity, I popped into the adjoining greengrocer section and saw that they were selling their lemons for five dollars a kilo. This confirmed it; I would knock at the door with the lemon tree and purchase some lemons for a tenth of the price of the shop. The smallest Italian bloke I have ever laid eyes on answered the door and told me that you get about half a dozen in a kilo, so I accepted. He took me into his garage and put some in a little bag for me. He looked at me and said, "I give you few extra." I only had a two-dollar coin, but I was still very happy because it was certainly still cheaper than the shops and they couldn't be any fresher! When I told him to keep the change, he looked horror-stricken and promptly started piling lemons into the bag and wouldn't stop when I asked him to, ignoring me stressing that I didn't want them to go to waste by rotting. I ended up with about forty lemons and they were all huge. With difficulty because my fingers were sore from flaring up, I got them back home and used some of the juice in my guacamole. It was delicious, even if I do say so myself. I ate a couple of slices and it really was one of the best lemons I had ever tasted. I became a little obsessed with lemon and avocado whilst living in Perth (hence making a lot of guacamole) and got cravings for both by the end of each week when we would run low on supplies. A greengrocer we found locally sold avocados at a fraction of the supermarket price and they were so much better in taste and quality. After noticing the weight I had put on with the steroids was finally coming off, I read that lemons increase the metabolism, especially if you eat the skin like I do. The little Italian bloke didn't use any sprays, so a good wash and the skin was fine to eat. With the surplus, I decided to make lemonade using a recipe I found on the internet. That way, they didn't go to waste by going mouldy and it tasted delicious. It turned out like a lemon syrup that you dilute with sparkling water.

My sick days consisted of hunting for a job that didn't require talking for seven hours or being on my feet, watching rented films from the local video store and resting.

One of the temp jobs I finally got after telesales was a sale day at a farm machinery auction. It was such an exciting experience, although the 5am alarm was painful, particularly because I was suffering with serious fatigue due to the arthritis. I was also in much more pain and had much more stiffness in my joints in the morning. But it was worth it as it was so much fun! Plus, the temping agency that got me the job asked me to work as an administrator for them afterwards. This was a compliment because they had masses of people on their books (I know because part of my job was to sort them), so I must have impressed!

We enjoyed a few great nights out during my temping days, but fairly often I'd be left in a huge amount of pain when my toes swelled up. One night in particular eight out of ten toes (the big ones being the lucky ones) swelled and I had to walk home in my bare, swollen feet. It could also be quite hard to get into the swing of dancing because of the pain, but also because I had to be sober whilst on my medication (particularly the methotrexate because of the liver-damaging side effects). I was hoping that I wouldn't have to be banned from drinking in the long term, and just hoped it was to get me back to a healthy place.

CHAPTER SEVEN

Spring at last?

October 2009

On my next specialist appointment all was as expected for me because I'd still been experiencing a lot of pain and stiffness in my joints. The medication I was injecting, Enbrel, wasn't working very well after the initial success of taking the edge off, so I was changed to a different kind of anti-TNF. The new one, Humira, was only to be injected once a fortnight, and it was a pen (like an allergy sufferer's epi-pen) rather than the syringes I'd been using and so less scary. I was to find out, however, that the pens were so much more painful than the needles with this medication at that time. This brand used citric acid as a preservative (which I believe has since been changed), which made the injection sting, but with the syringes you could control how slowly you injected and make it hurt a bit less. The pens just rammed it all in at once. At the end of the three-month probation period I was promised that I could be signed off on a six-month supply if I attended the rheumatology appointment they'd make me in Sydney and have plenty to travel home with. Otherwise it would have been a bit of a struggle because I'd have had to make do with the methotrexate tablets that only worked on my fingers and toes and I may have been more restricted on travel activities than I was hoping to be. I thought at the time that, if that was to happen, I'd be hiring myself someone to carry my backpack for me!

The spring brought another menace. Adam and I were both suffering with hay fever. I had only had it once before in my life, so it took four weeks to realise it wasn't just a cold. It wasn't good for Adam who was working as a landscape gardener as well as helping out our landlord to save money on his rent. We both managed to find tablets that worked brilliantly, though, and managed to get it under control. One of the pharmacists I spoke to was English and said that most English people she knew got hay fever in Australia really badly, regardless of whether or not they suffered in England, because the Australian pollen is so alien to English bodies. It may also have been down to my suppressed immune system that I was struggling. With only nine weeks until we were back on the road, we were happy to have it under control and were busily saving the pennies and counting down the days until we were backpacking again. The Oz travel plans had to change the most because of my extenuating circumstances, so we now only had a month to drive across the country. This meant that we were to go across the south coast, missing out the centre, including the trip to Uluru, and were only to get as north on the east coast as Sydney (from where we were to fly to New Zealand). I was desperate to dive on the Great Barrier Reef, but that would just have to wait for a future trip. Also, I knew that it would probably be a good idea to be in remission before I could dive again and, even then, I didn't know if I'd be able to get the insurance to do so. I still don't, so answers on a postcard please!

One morning, the forecast had said it would be thirty-two degrees centigrade later in the day and, at 9am, the sun was already burning hot. We headed to Mandurah, which is quite a way south of the city. We went to the beach, which had sand banks going out for miles. While the boys waded off the sand banks to fish, I happily sunbathed, ensuring that I was loaded up with sun cream because one of the side effects of my injections was making me more susceptible to skin cancer. I went a bit brown, but not very much because I was being very careful. It was great to fully relax, though. The boys caught dozens of whiting and we took home several that were good enough to eat. Aaron gutted them and cooked them Thai style with lots of chilli. They were very tasty, but the next day I had a frightful tummy bug. It seemed a bit fishy (like the pun?!) that it was the third time I'd had fish in the previous couple of months and every time I ended up not being able to leave the bathroom for a good while afterwards. I was really hoping it was not an allergy due to my fond affection for the meats of the sea. Luckily it seemed it was just a temporary side effect of the medications I was on and I was able to happily eat seafood after a few months.

I was sad to leave the recruitment agency, but unfortunately I worked myself out of my job by being too efficient at the data entry role and there wasn't enough work for me. As the regularity of my paycheques were decreasing, my bills at the chemist seemed to be increasing. My doctor said my new prescription would be with me a few days after he'd sent it off to Tasmania for the powers that be at Medicare to sign and post it to me. After two weeks of fruitless post box checking, I gave the doctor's receptionist a call. She called Tasmania and was told it had been posted on the 15th October and so, if I hadn't received it, it must be lost in the mail. This meant that my doctor had to write a new prescription to post for them to sign and then post it to me... again. Meanwhile, my old medication was coming out of my system, so my joints were becoming increasingly balloon-like. I thought it could be worse, though. At least I was still on the tablets, so I was not as bad as I would have been without anything. My fingers were luckily flexible enough to type. Therefore, my trip to the chemist consisted of extra strong painkillers, cortisone cream for my psoriasis, which had reared its ugly head on the back of my knees just in time for the skirt season, and hay fever medication. But I counted myself lucky. Of all the places to have bad luck, Australia is probably one of the places you wouldn't mind having it. After all, what better place to rest your sore feet than on the beach?! Also, in my opinion, you cannot get a much more efficient medical system.

Aaron had also been suffering quite a bit, so I was desperately trying not to moan. He was coughing his guts up for over a week, so I made him a doctor's appointment so that he'd have to go. It turned out it was a good job I did because he had a virus that left him with a chest infection. He was put on antibiotics, and they worked quickly, but it took him a long time to get over the after-effects of it.

The actual work front had been a bit odd. After having weeks of relentlessly applying to jobs with no joy, I got several calls from various agencies. They were all calling because I'd applied for jobs on career websites that were put up by them. They all gave the same blurb that was basically 'the position you applied for has been filled, but we would like you to come in and register so that we can hopefully find you some work'. One of them provided the longest interview ever. It started at 10am with some very in-depth questions about what work I liked, my qualities, etc. Then I had to fill in all the usual paperwork such as bank details. The problem I kept coming across in temp agency paperwork was that they all ask for a health questionnaire to be filled out and if you don't answer truthfully then this will void your insurance because you have to sign and date it. This potentially meant that I could lose a finger in a rogue stapler incident and not be entitled to any help if I hadn't declared my new disease. It begged the question of whether it was restricting my temp job opportunities to have this diagnosis looming over my paperwork. After all, I registered with many agencies and had very little luck. So, with a glum outlook on the job opportunities, I then had to complete a series of tests including Word, Excel and typing speed. I annoyed myself in the data entry because I was doing very well (about sixty words per minute being my usual) until I accidentally pressed enter instead of space and messed up a whole page. This brought my word count down to a disappointing forty-six words per minute and the final smidge of hope I had for this agency was quashed. She said that she'd keep looking for me and we bid goodbye with me fully expecting never to hear from her again and feeling like that was an hour and a half of my life that I'd never get back. I thought myself lucky that at least I had a night's work waitressing at a function on that weekend and just hoped that my back would be able to cope with it. The next day, to my utter surprise, I got a call from a wee Scotsman called Kenny saying that he had a job and Mary, the lady who had interviewed me the day before, had recommended me for it. It was five days' work due to start the next day. It was in a mail room in the Chamber of Commerce and he said the duties would be sorting, letter stuffing and some data entry.

My dad was good enough to text me a little anecdote of his time in a mail room when I informed him of my new job. He said that he had to wear anti-blast gear because the IRA had a letter bombing campaign going on. So, with that confidence boost, but mostly with much excitement, I dressed up in the gorgeous suit I bought for a tenner from the Salvation Army shop and headed to the Chamber of Commerce to start my new temp position. The building itself was impressive. It was a couple of CAT bus stops (CAT stands for Central Area Transit) away from the WACA, the famous cricket ground, and it was all open plan, lots of glass and lots of expensive-looking art. I was greeted in reception by Leon, a little Indian guy with a smashing accent who was the team leader. I was then introduced to the other guys in the office: Noel from Mauritius and Kevin from New Zealand. I was shown around the very smart office, given a cup of tea and told to relax until they'd organised themselves. It turned out they hadn't expected the agency to come up with a temp so fast and they were also having a crisis. The handbook I was supposed to stuff into envelopes along with address sheets had an amendment on the first sheet. 300 copies had already been printed, so lone front sheets had to be printed for those copies and then whole books for the rest of the 3000 clients. So, for my first day, I stuffed envelopes for a different mail shot of only about 300, which needed a letter, two fliers and an address sheet to be in line with the window of the envelope. This was supposed to take me all day, so I paced myself (I didn't want to work myself out of another job!).

Noel and Kevin took it in turns to keep me company and I thoroughly enjoyed getting to know them; they were very interesting. I had recently read *Golden Bats and Pink Pigeons* by Gerald Durrell, one of my amazing charity bookshop finds, which was all about his expeditions in the seventies to Mauritius to help conserve the dwindling populations of bats and pigeons that were down to a matter of hundreds. He also helped a couple of breeds of skink (including the Telfair) and a type of boa on the Mauritian islands, two of which were called Round Island and Snake Island. This information gave me some good conversation material on the topic of Mauritius, a country which is very much on my travel list after reading the book. I asked him if it was true that Round Island and Snake Island are mixed up on the map; Mr Durrell said that Round Island isn't round and has snakes and Snake Island is round and doesn't have snakes! Unfortunately, he only knew of Round Island, so couldn't say (although he could confirm the lack of roundness and inhabitancy of snakes). He says that there are so many little islands that the locals weren't really interested in until relatively recently when the tourist industry boomed. The population was approximately 1.2 million, with an additional tourist population of 1 million! We discussed the detrimental effect tourism has on the environment and my internal conflict that I think it's terrible, yet still want to go and visit, which would make me part of the problem! He told me all about the reefs, which Gerald Durrell was so fascinated in. He also told me all about the diverse cuisine, which was influenced by the many different cultures that invaded over the centuries, as well as their neighbours. It sounded fantastic (the food part, not the invasion part). He even had a calendar on his desk of Mauritian birds that had won the battle to beat endangerment and I was ecstatic to see that the eponymous pink pigeon of my book was one of them – Gerald Durrell had succeeded again! Noel was very interested in him as he had never heard of him, so when I left, I gave him the book.

Kevin kept me entertained with discussions on Australia and New Zealand, where he came from a farming background. It was a very busy office, though (the recession meant they cut staff numbers and they had three people to do six people's work) and in the long periods I was on my own I couldn't help but work at a normal pace and found myself finishing in the early afternoon. So, I relieved Noel from the folding machine that needed to be babysat because every fourth letter decided to jam it up; he was about to kill it. I couldn't really blame it for protesting. It was getting on a bit and had the task to fold letters and stuff them into envelopes for a twelve thousand letter mail shot. My last task was to stamp all the envelopes for my stuffing tasks the next day with a postage paid stamp – thoroughly stimulating work, but I really enjoyed it! I finished the day feeling very happy having had a really lovely first day of work meeting very interesting new people.

Not long after I'd started the new anti-TNF medication, it was a lot easier to get out of bed and my fingers nearly got back to their normal size. My feet were less painful too and my back was a touch better, so I was crossing my fingers that it would continue along the path to normal joint size.

L'Anniversaire: 14/11/2009

When I wrote the blog entry telling my friends and family about mine and Aaron's anniversary shenanigans, I started it by thanking him for such a great day and a fantastic two years together. I also apologised to anyone with a sensitive disposition and warned them that the entry may get a bit gushy! The same applies to this chapter. I had such an amazing time travelling and the anniversary celebrations were particularly memorable.

Our anniversary technically began the night before the big day. For the first time in a long time, I actually managed to stay awake long enough to see midnight to hear him say, 'Happy anniversary,' and fall into a very pleasant night's sleep. I'd been having complex dreams and one recurring dream in particular had been disturbing my sleep, but I slept so well and so heavily that I didn't notice Aaron's alarm going off or him getting up the next morning. The first thing I was aware of was him waking me up very excitedly saying that he had been awake since 6.30am because he was too excited and was now getting bored!

Eventually, after a lot of irritation at being woken up at 9am after a late night and still feeling tired and stiff, I roused myself enough to get up to make him breakfast. As I crossed the hallway to the bathroom, I glanced into the living room and stopped in my tracks. Lying on the couch was a white box about a metre by half a metre big with an oval window and a little envelope on top. As I got closer, I saw that the envelope had my name on it and, through the window, I could see green foliage and a flash of crimson. I called for Aaron and he came in with a sheepish look on his face as I said, "What have you done? We said no presents!" But, as I opened the very pretty card and opened the box to reveal a dozen beautiful long-stemmed roses, a huge grin flashed across my face and I thanked him, knowing that it was the start to a very special day. Roses are my absolute favourite flowers and are special to me because Rose is my middle name, which is passed down through the women in my mum's side of the family. It is a tradition that I love (and one that I have now continued with my first daughter, Lily Rose) and they are truly beautiful. It also made me giggle because Aaron was very excited that they were wrapped in purple wrapping; his favourite colour! The only problem was trying to come up with a way to display them as we did not have a vase in the house. Aaron produced the kettle from our campervan and wrapped the purple wrapping to conceal it. It worked wonderfully and I was incredibly happy.

Before getting ready for the day ahead, I got to work on the bacon and fried egg sandwich I had planned for him. The difficult part was keeping a very restless Aaron out of the kitchen. I had a table booked for us at the C Restaurant, which was the revolving restaurant at the top of the Amcom tower. The problem was the same issue that I have every time I plan a surprise for him. I had to ask Aaron to request the day off work, so then he kept badgering me as to the reason why and somehow managed to guess where we were going. For this reason, I wanted to do a little something that he would never guess. I bought an egg ring in the shape of a heart and it worked fantastically well. I left the sandwich open to display this work of art but Aaron went to dive right in! He then asked me why I was looking at him funny and I knew that he hadn't noticed, so I had to point it out to him! It was a very cheesy moment, but at least one that he hadn't expected (or noticed, for that matter!). I got ready with some gorgeous purple eyeliner and eyeshadow that were a steal in the sales. This was to go with the dress that I had hidden in Adam's wardrobe. I originally got a dress in the sales for forty dollars (about twenty quid), but wasn't happy because it was a little snug around the chest and it didn't make me feel confident. Luckily, the day before, I walked past a tiny boutique that advertised a sale and had lots of purple shining in the window. I found a pretty dress that was an absolute bargain at twenty dollars (about a tenner) and a waist belt for seven dollars (about £3.50) that made me feel a million dollars. I got all dolled up, took some painkillers so that I could wear my high heels (that was the only way I could stand them with my swollen toes!) and emerged from the bedroom to a look on Aaron's face that was exactly what I was after! The fact that the dress was purple was really all that it would have taken, but he was very flattering with his compliments, so I was very happy. I will forever be gutted that I took the dress to be dry cleaned after that night and forgot to pick it up before we left Perth.

I felt a little bit silly hopping on the bus and walking through the city at lunchtime looking totally over-dressed, but by the time we got to the restaurant in the Central Business District, we were surrounded by equally dressed-up people, so all was good. It was a little baffling trying to get into the building because the main revolving doors were closed at weekends, but once we found the side door we were on our way. My heart was racing as we arrived on the thirty-third floor and even more so when we were led to our table by the window. Aaron sat at the window and I was round the corner of the table to calm myself down by not being so close to the massive drop. After a few minutes, I had relaxed enough to happily enjoy the amazing views. It was a weird sensation because the restaurant revolved at a rate that was quite noticeable, but the ever-changing views were fantastic. At one stage, we could see the Bank West tower, where I had had an interview on the forty-second of the forty-six floors (I was glad not to get that one!). We could also see Burswood, where Aaron was working. We tried to spot our house, but they were all too tiny to distinguish our modest unit. I had booked us for high tea, so the waitress came over with our glass of sparkling wine (with a cherry on the side) and took our tea order. I went with the traditional English breakfast, which I love, and Aaron went with the much-needed caffeine boost of percolated coffee! Having not drunk sparkling wine since England, the bubbles went straight to my head.

When the tiered silver platter was brought out I was a little disappointed that the writing on one of the cakes that I was promised (the lady I booked with was going to write 'Happy Anniversary Aaron' on one of the cakes) was non-existent and the waitress embarrassed me a little bit by saying, "I didn't put the sparkler on because I didn't think you'd be able to see it in the daytime, do you want it anyway?" I held my decorum and politely declined, seeing as the surprise element had evaporated. The food made up for it, though, because it was magnificent. The tiny finger sandwiches were deceptively filling, the mini quiches a taste sensation and the cakes and scones... well, we pushed ourselves to the point of throwing-up-feeling-fullness simply to taste them! The teeny cakes were absolutely delightful.

We left to take a stroll along the river because Aaron had booked us a table at a restaurant in the evening and we had a lot of time to kill. We also needed to let our cake go down. I had with me a bag big enough to hold my shoes, so I happily changed into my flip flops. It may have looked ridiculous with my pretty dress, but the heat (it was high twenties) swelling up my feet on top of their existing swollenness meant vanity was not an option. As we reached the piers, Aaron told me what he had originally planned. He had planned to take me on a river cruise, but when he had tried to book a month ago, they were already fully booked. On the off-chance that they had had cancellations, he tried again while we were there and was very excited to hear that five places had freed up, so he got his wish and he cancelled our restaurant reservation. We had two hours before boarding, so we headed back into town to go to Aaron's favourite pub, which was a Belgian Bar. We had a drink while listening to the live music, then headed back to a very classy pub on the waterfront called "The Lucky Shag". Hmmm… the lovely setting didn't exactly go with the name, but we had a nice little drink there anyway. I asked one of the locals if the name meant what it does in England and it turns out that it does, although Aussies don't use that word very often.

We got to the pier about ten minutes prior to the boarding time so that we could be the first there and get a good seat. It worked and we sat on the front seats opposite the captain with our first complimentary glass of wine. The skipper was very entertaining as he did his little spiel as we left the pier to begin the cruise. He informed us that all the alcohol was complimentary on our way to the restaurant and while we were there, but not on the way home. He warned us to enjoy ourselves, but to be careful because he had the power to leave people behind if he thought they were too intoxicated. I had two glasses, so had had four altogether by the time we got to the restaurant and felt pretty darn merry, seeing as it was the most I had drunk in six months. When we arrived, we were checked off the list and given a table number. There was a very large party of fifty that had big tables and we were surprised to find our table set for three. It was also a little bit odd to find Christmas crackers on all the tables. A gentleman with a Yorkshire accent joined us and introduced himself as Steve. He apologised, saying that he was in Perth on business and would ask to move if we wanted the table to ourselves. Of course, we said, 'Oh no, it's fine,' made jokes about being together so long we had nothing to talk about anyway and welcomed him to our table, but it was a bit weird at first. However, after a short while of getting to know him, we were having a blast and there were no longer any regrets about being polite. The food was a sumptuous buffet, the wine flowed and we had a really good time. I only had a glass of wine, but was very, very merry. We pulled our crackers and I was content with my false moustache, but disappointed when I realised later that none of us read our jokes. I have a penchant for terrible jokes! Eventually, we were all kicked out and thrown back on the boat for the journey back. This time, we sat on the deck at the front of the boat and chatted to lots of the people who had been at the big tables. It was a work party and a couple of them gave Aaron and I some tips on where to go along the South Coast, none of which either of us could remember the following day. Steve came out and joined us for a drink and another chat. We exchanged numbers and it would have been lovely to see him again and maybe meet his family, seeing as we felt that we knew so much about them, but we never got round to it. It was all so fun that we didn't want the night to end when we left the boat at 11.30pm.

Meanwhile, Adam had been enjoying a night out with our new next-door neighbour Becks. It was her birthday and she had no one to celebrate with, so he took her out for drinks and his work mates were supposed to join them. He also asked us to join them when we were done, so we gave them a call. We met up with them outside the Mustang Bar and it turned out that none of his work mates had turned up. We decided to head somewhere else as the bar had a queue to get back in and it was incredibly busy inside. I changed my shoes (I had put my heels back on for the cruise and my poor toes were suffering) and then we headed to the first club that had no queue, which was called Impact. They were playing dance music and we boogied the night away. Becks was lovely and a lot of fun, so it was a great finish to a good night. When we left, though, Becks disappeared. We were very worried as none of us had her number and she was tiny, pretty and was highly inebriated in Northbridge, which is a very scary place at that time on a weekend. We debated for a while what our options were because she could have gone home or could have been in trouble. I realised our only option was to give our landlady a call to see if she had her phone number because none of us did. I felt guilty because it was 1.40am, but I couldn't see any other way of making sure she was okay. Luckily Kathy was still up, so we didn't wake her. She gave us Becks' number and we found her leaving a kebab house (classy bird, I knew I liked her!) and I called Kathy again to let her know Becks was safe, as she'd requested, and apologised again for disturbing her. We then had to wait for over an hour at a taxi rank because the only number there was to book a taxi resulted in them telling you to wait in the taxi rank queues. No wonder there was always violence in Northbridge at the weekends. The queue was filled with very angry and increasingly impatient people who just wanted to get to bed and sleep off the alcohol. I couldn't understand why they didn't improve on the absence of taxis in the city at the weekends, particularly when people were crying out for jobs. By the time we got home, I was shattered and crashed out in bed. It had been one of the most fun days of my life.

The next morning, I was racked with guilt because I was sick. I realised I had had five glasses of wine and a cocktail and put my body at risk because I was not supposed to drink on my medication. I felt fine after I threw up, but the guilt was awful. It was a one off, though, and didn't happen again. My next mistake was to satisfy the McDonalds craving I had developed throughout the day by getting 'Drive-Thru'. The strawberry milkshake I ordered had been mixed with coffee, which I hated at the time, and therefore couldn't drink. The Big Mac also tasted a bit funny, but I was so hungry I just ate it. Subsequently, I spent about an hour being very ill indeed and full of regret. So I went to bed feeling very sorry for myself and clutching my cramping stomach.

CHAPTER EIGHT

On the Road Again

I got a call from the temp agency that got me the mailroom job in the Chamber of Commerce. Kenny had got me a temp job starting the following morning as a group administrator for Golder Associates. I arrived twenty minutes early the next morning and the receptionist had no idea who I was or that there was supposed to be a new temp starting. I had asked for Bryony, who Kenny had told me to ask for, but she wasn't anywhere to be found. Kate, the very nice receptionist, rang around trying to find out where I was supposed to be and found out that I was supposed to be meeting Amanda, but she couldn't be found either. It wasn't a great start to the day. Eventually I was sent down to the first floor (the reception was on the second floor) to meet Ivan. He took me around the floor and I met the few people that were in that day; most of the floor was away 'in the field'. I was introduced to my new desk, which I was to take over from Amanda to be the new Group Administrator for the Environment department. Golder is a company that looks after lots of projects, such as mining and building projects. The environment department assesses the type of environment for which the project is planned and the impact it will have on the environment. This involves lots of project paperwork as well as the normal company admin required. This was not all very clear to me on my first day. When Ivan showed me my desk, Amanda came in and apologised for being late, but she had to go to the doctors with an eye infection, which made me slightly anxious since I was on immunosuppressants and didn't particularly want to be near ill people! She was changing positions to work on a project on the ground floor called Wheatstone and had been effectively dealing with both jobs for a while. She had several Wheatstone meetings that day and so the training I was supposed to be receiving was very bitty and I felt a bit silly being there because I had no idea what I was supposed to be doing. I felt a bit lost.

The next day, however, was much better. It started with a training session in 'word processing'. This was the procedure for formatting documents to fit with the Golder structure with the aim that one should never be able to tell by whom it was written (they call it 'Golderising'). It is a complicated process as they use templates and the process to make any changes to documents consists of several steps. In my future career in book publishing I was to realise they'd have been much better using typesetting software like InDesign rather than word processing software, so it was good training in what not to do! I took notes and Claire (the trainer) gave us a great handbook. I didn't expect to use it, though, because there is a word processor for each department, but we were being trained in case they were overloaded or weren't there when a document was urgent. That day I also had some training in the short space of time that Amanda had to spare and was shown how to bind documents by Karen, the reprographics lady, in case she wasn't there. Then I had training on how to create documents using the Golder templates. I also had the IT induction from Josh and he was happy he could skip through most of the PowerPoint slides because I knew most things already. He set up my desktop and my email and sent me an email to show me how to set up my signature and how to use the company website. The last training of the day was Amanda showing me how to deal with invoices. It was a good day and I felt much more confident about the job. I had a better idea of what was required of me; Amanda said the job description was basically whatever no one else wanted to do! She was also kind enough to tell me it was casual day on Fridays and I could wear jeans and flip-flops. I still found it weird when they called them thongs. My toes were very happy to learn of their imminent freedom because my swollen toes weren't particularly comfortable in shoes.

Friday was the first day I actually felt like the job was mine. Amanda was due to move down to the ground floor in the afternoon. We finished off the invoice training and various bits and bobs. She had written a handbook and had it bound for me, which was very useful. I had a good chat with Sue, who was the word processor for the department. She was from Wigan originally, but had no sign of the accent because she had lived in Australia for so long. At 11.30am I attended my first departmental meeting to take notes. The procedure for note-taking was very straightforward. I had to print off two copies of the previous meeting's minutes, one for me and one for whoever was leading the meeting, which was usually Ivan, the environment project manager. The meetings were normally very similar, so I just had to mark the changes on the minutes and that was all. After that, Amanda took her keyboard (it was a special ergonomic one and I was glad to see the back of it because it was very difficult for me to use. I still prefer a standard keyboard because the ergonomic ones put pressure on the wrong places of my wrists and hands when they're swollen) and hard drive downstairs. While I waited for my new hardware to arrive, I took my lunch break and headed to the roof for the weekly barbeque hoping to meet some new people. I got my wish and met several new people including Penny from my floor, who was from the east coast and lived for a couple of years in Canada. I also met Alma, an administrator for another department and we had a good old chat. There was a man with a bushy beard who told the group to shield their eyes and look twoards the sun. It was one of the most fascinating natural sights I had ever seen. There was a thick, dark ring around the sun, with a thin halo of light around that. It was strangely beautiful and he said it was a very unusual sight, but it was ice crystals forming above 300 000 feet. I've since researched and found it could have been what's called a 22° halo. I wish it had been possible to photograph it; it was amazing.

When I got back from eating a delicious burger cooked on the company barbeque, Ivan came over to my desk. Sue was out to lunch and he had a letter that needed word processing urgently, but didn't have time to do it. He asked if I could word process and I said I'd had the training, but hadn't put it into practice yet. I said I would be happy to do it, but it may take me a while. So, he gave me the opportunity to put my new skills to good use. I was happy that the training was not in vain, seeing as I was only there a few weeks. It took me until 4.30pm to complete the task (which included converting to PDF, which took a while because I didn't have the right software), but he was happy with my work because I picked up a couple of errors that he'd missed and sorted a few problems. Perhaps a precursor for my future career in editing! I was happy with my first attempt and felt I would be a lot quicker next time. At 4.30pm every Friday, they had a technical presentation in the boardroom, but people really went for the free drinks and nibbles! Australians really know the best way to work. They have work parties during office hours for anything. I particularly enjoyed the Melbourne Cup party, which was the equivalent to our Grand National, but held on a weekday to give people an excuse to skive work. They had drinks and nibbles for this with the race shown on the big screens. They had a pool where you paid a few dollars and pulled a horse out of the hat. Even though I didn't win, it was still a lot of fun to meet more people, have a drink and have a giggle during work hours. All in all, after a slow and uncertain start, I felt much better about my new job.

Last Week of Perth: 12/12/2009

My last day of work at Golder Associates was a little bit sad for a few reasons. Firstly, I missed out on the weekly barbeque on the Friday because the house needed to be cleaned and packed up as we were due to leave on Friday afternoon. Secondly, everyone at work was lovely and it was the best job I'd had in Australia. My boss said that I was a great addition to the team and they were miffed that I had to go. I could see myself working there for a long time and would have had ambitions to work up to be a project manager. It was a great compliment from him, but if it was a choice between Margaret River and work, what would you do? So, I tied up all my loose ends, including producing a clearer instruction manual for my replacement, and said goodbye to some great people. Then I headed home to find Adam stressing about the van. It turned out that, in the space of a week, our radiator and starter motor both went. We had brand new ones fitted (after getting the new starter motor replaced because they gave us a faulty one) and she was running again. Aaron and I then headed out to celebrate our last night in Perth (Adam was working on the Friday, so couldn't join us). As he had ceased employment with Burswood for more than twenty-four hours, Aaron was allowed to gamble again, so we decided to have an ultra-cheap night at the casino. I had forty-five dollars in my pocket, which would cover dinner and gambling and I planned on getting home with at least half still intact. We headed to the Riviera Room where Aaron used to work to say hi to his ex-colleagues. This was where we spent most of the night because if you put the occasional dollar in the machines, you got free drinks. I had stopped taking methotrexate (because the Humira injections were effective enough to work alone),which was the medication that I couldn't drink on the week before so, although I was being careful, I was allowed a couple. I had sparkling wine and Aaron's mate gave me two cherries and a strawberry, so she was instantly my friend! We sat on a gaming machine called *Keno*. I had to choose ten numbers and the machine dropped them down some tubes. If the numbers got higher than a mark on the screen you won a bit of money and each level above it was worth more. I put a ten dollar note in (around five pounds sterling at the time) and it didn't take me long to treble my money!

We got a bit hungry and joined Club Burswood (it was free to do), which gave us discounts off our food. It meant that I could then use my winnings to buy Aaron and me dinner. We pottered around for a bit getting free drinks, and then ended up back on the Keno machines. Again, I put a tenner in and that would be the last of my gambling money for the night. One of the rows got above the win line and it kept on going. To my astonishment, it got up to the ninety dollar mark! I immediately cashed it in to Aaron's annoyance because I didn't know that if you called a staff member over, they could give you the notes. Instead, I sat there for ages as my little gold coins dropped down one by one and I was squealing with excitement whilst Aaron was embarrassedly shushing me and trying to get me to calm down. I went to the cashier and changed fifty of them into a note, so that I wouldn't spend it and I would definitely go home up for the night. I gave Aaron an allowance to play with and, after we played around for a bit, we only had half an hour before our train home. We played my favourite table game *two ups*. I was desperate to play one game as it was the only place it was played and it was doubtful I'd ever get the chance again. With our new Club Burswood cards we could get a five dollar gaming voucher each. The two ups table had a ten dollar minimum, so we pooled our free chips together and put them all on tails. The random gambler who'd been chosen to throw the two coins in the air got two no go results where they came back with a head and a tail. On the third throw, to my amazement, it landed with both coins on tails: our chips were doubled! We then headed to the roulette table and put one of the five dollar chips on black to keep Aaron happy as we had to leave. After a tense few moments where the ball span round the little wheel, it landed on black, we thanked the croupier, grabbed our chips and ran for the train as we were now running late! I ended up going home with twenty dollars more than when I arrived, even though I'd fed us and paid for our transport. It was a great night and very weird to spend a lot of money yet get home with more in my pocket.

Unfortunately, the night ended on a sour note as we witnessed an assault on the bus ride home and had to go to the police station for them to file the reports. So, after planning to get home by 12.30am and get to bed to get up early to clean, we ended up home at 3am, full of jolly robins (my mum's phrase for a head full of stuff like robins tweeting round your head when you're trying to get to sleep) and overslept in the morning. We cleaned the house and packed our stuff, I gave all my work clothes and the books I'd read to the charity shop down the road and I headed to the supermarket to replace the ridiculous amount of crockery and cups the clumsy boys had smashed. Luckily, they had a sale and I got a sixteen-piece set including cups for twenty bucks (the cheapest single plate was four dollars). Adam got home late after sorting out the faulty new starter motor at the garage, packed and we got our bond (deposit) back from the landlady before setting off at about 8pm. This was a lot later than we intended, but we were very happy to be leaving at last. It had been a very eventful last week, which was bound to happen, really, given the eventfulness of our whole stay in Perth. Although we had such good times in our little house there, we were very happy to finally be backpackers again. With only ten weeks until we were due to go home, it was going to be a very exciting next couple of months.

Maggie River

Shortly after leaving our house in Perth, we passed the dry cleaners and I got very upset because we realised that I had forgotten to pick up my anniversary dress from there; I had planned to wear it on New Year's Eve, but it was shut, so I wasn't happy! Halfway to Margaret River, the boys got very upset because they realised that when they had re-sprayed the van, they had taken the tube with the fishing rods in it off the front of the van and forgotten to put it back. It was still resting against the fence at our old house! So, we were all upset by our rubbish memories. We arrived at the campsite just after 11pm, having made fantastic time driving from Perth. We strapped the head torches on, set up the tent and had a beer before retiring to bed as we were all shattered.

In the morning, we all awoke early due to a combination of an early night to bed, light streaming into the van and the tent as the sun rose plus the raucous noise of the birds, which included the lamenting squall of the crows and the singsong chirping of the parrots. We headed off to the reception where we had to officially check in and pay for the three nights we were staying. The night before, they had left the key in the post box for us because we would be checking in after the reception closed. I also had to ask them to keep my anti-TNF medication (which had to be refrigerated, so had been in our Eski up to that point) in their private fridge for me for fear of children getting to it in the public one, and was grateful that they were very happy to oblige. We then headed out to check out the little town, book ourselves on a winery tour, which we thought would have to be for the following day, and find something for breakfast. The information centre was lovely and the town of Margaret River was a lot bigger than I expected. To our delight, they had spaces on the tour that day and we had less than an hour to get back to our campsite (from which the tour bus would pick us up), get ready and have breakfast. This meant we just picked up a bacon roll from the nearby bakery instead of buying proper food, but it was lovely! We were outside our campsite slopped in sun cream because it was forecast to be thirty-seven degrees in Perth. Maggie River is usually three degrees cooler than Perth, but it felt like it got close to forty during the day. The minibus papped its horn and we jumped on. We were introduced to the gang by Silvano, the driver, and then he told us everyone's name. He had a freaky memory! We picked up a few more people and there ended up being twenty of us on the tour. Silvano was very entertaining and had a great sense of humour as he told us a bit about the region.

The first vineyard we stopped at was called Haystead Farm. The tasting room looked pretty modern and we were very excited to get our first wine to try. We started on whites and moved through rosé to the reds. This was the order of all the tastings. We tried eleven different wines and I was already feeling pretty tipsy at midday! I got talking to quite a few of the people on our tour, including a girl called Robyn, a German guy from her hostel and a few of the older couples. Everyone was very nice and chatty. We then headed to our second winery called Brookwood Estate. This was my favourite winery of the day and not just because this is where we had our lunch! We tried about six or seven wines and we even bought a bottle from them because they were all so good. I even liked the Chenin Blanc, which I normally really dislike. The lunch was fabulous and included a selection of cold meats (including kangaroo), salads and bread. It was very filling, but delicious. To finish, we all had to eat *Bush limes,* which are tiny berries that have a faintly limey, but very bitter taste. Aboriginals eat them to aid digestion after a meal. Only four people were allowed pudding and they were the first to raise their hands after we each got a good look at it. Adam was chosen. It was long, fat, white and had little legs close to its ugly head. For those who haven't guessed what it is yet, it was a witchetty grub. When asked what it tasted like, he replied that it tasted like witchetty grub! It turned out that it tasted nutty, but, as he is allergic to them, he wouldn't really know what nuts taste like because it'd been so long since he'd tried them.

From there, it was on to Tassle Park winery where we tried a lovely mulled wine at the end. It then started to sink in a tiny bit how close Christmas was, despite the heat. It was also there that I heard the phrase of the day from the host. She said, 'There is no such thing as monogamy when it comes to wine,' when someone said that they only normally like one type of wine and were surprised with the variety they enjoyed. From there we went to a brewery, called Cowaramup Brewery, where sadly they were not allowed to include the tasting on the wine tour. Luckily, our tour got a discount and for eleven dollars we could try four midi-midis of beer and one of their seasonal special stout (that was the only one that I didn't like very much). It was a lot of fun and we sat on a table in the garden and got to know Dave and his wife plus Robyn and the German guy. It was here that a child of about eight years of age came over with a shy-sounding voice and guilted us into buying stickers to save the koalas! On the way to the cheese factory, we had a sing song and were all tipsy enough not to care how cheesy (sorry!) it was. My favourite cheese was a marinated feta, which was fabulous. It was then on to our final winery called Churchview (guess why!) where I got to sip wine whilst stroking an absolutely gorgeous long-haired tabby kitten, which was lapping up the attention in its air-conditioned paradise.

To finish the tour, we were taken to the Margaret River chocolate factory where we could eat as many free chocolate drops as we could. We certainly felt sick after that. We then headed back to drop off the Kiwis who were the last group to get on in the morning. They were sitting in front of us and Kirsty was kind enough to drop a piece of paper on my lap containing her contact details, so that we could have a tour guide when we were to get to Rotorua in New Zealand. Unfortunately, we never got around to contacting her, but it was a lovely gesture. It was here that everyone was given back their wines and cheeses that were kept in cool bags for the tour. Adam had bought half a case of label-less wine, which was flogged off cheaply due to the absence of labels. They had thrown in a free bottle, so we ended up taking eight bottles home and two small pieces of cheese. Adam was presented with a neck wine holder for being welcomed to the select group of "grubbies". He said that he was now officially a "grubby bastard"! We headed home very happy, stayed at the campsite for about twenty minutes, and then headed out to the local pub to meet up with some people from the tour. We ended up staying there all night and it was a fantastic finish to what had been a thoroughly enjoyable day.

Augusta and Pemberton

On the day we left Margaret River, we got up early, packed the van up and left the campsite for the nearby town of Augusta. On our way out of Margaret River, we stopped to get petrol. Adam asked the best way to get to Augusta and the bloke gave us a little map and said, 'It's just one road to get anywhere, mate; the roads here were built for drunks!' Arriving in Augusta, down the windy coastal road with views of the blue and green sea, we visited the lighthouse where the Southern and the Indian Oceans meet. We took a few photos, soaked up the scenery and stretched our legs before getting back in the van for the 150km drive to Pemberton. Adam's air bed deflated the night before and sleeping on concrete had made him very tired, so I was the driver for the day and the boys had to get cosy in the two passenger seats (the front of the van consisted of one bench, with all three seats across); they loved it really! The roads to Pemberton (there was only one turn the whole way) were very hilly and very windy, which made for a lovely, scenic drive through the wineries and then the forests.

We had a handy little brochure of all the campsites in the South West and arrived at the only one in Pemberton at about midday. We checked in for two nights and couldn't believe the beauty of the scene surrounding our pitch. We were on the far side of the camp, which was a tad annoying when we were desperate for the toilet as they were a bit of a walk away, but lovely because we were next to the brook. The weather had cooled a little from the weekend, but it was still in the early thirties and the mosquitoes and bluebottles had us doing the Aussie salute an annoying number of times. We had some great mosquito coils, though, and soon we were enjoying the incense-like aroma and were again able to enjoy the view. A family of ornate little ducks came to join us at our pitch and we enjoyed a sumptuous lunch of two-minute noodles with a bottle of wine. Then it was time to explore the wee town for the afternoon.

It was like a scene from a movie set in the Deep South of America; Pemberton was like stepping back in time. All the little wooden houses had verandas and we fully expected the old people sitting on the seats on their porches to be holding shotguns and chewing a piece of wheat. Instead, they nodded politely at us and we climbed the steep hill to find the information centre. We crossed an amusingly old-style railway crossing where one of the tracks had a mossy set of carriages rooted a little distance up and the other was also fairly overgrown. We found the information centre and ventured in. They had a musty-smelling museum that required a dollar donation. I poked my nose in, but didn't have a dollar and felt too guilty going in without giving it. There was one main thing that we wanted to do the following day and that was to climb the highest tree. Well, when I say "we", you do realise that the boys wanted to, and I would be the official photographer and possession holder. I had thought that it was only the Gloucester tree that you could climb. This was the highest fire watch point in Australia and you climb up metal pegs that coil around the fifty-eight metre high body of the trunk. That was trumped, however, by the Bicentennial tree, named after a chap called Dave Evans. This stands at a mighty seventy-five metres tall and is scarier than the Gloucester tree three-fold: it's higher, it has no protruding branches until the top and there is no ranger to look after it. "No thanks" was my opinion, but the boys were very excited. The lady who gave me loads of information on them was very helpful and showed me exactly where to go on the maps she gave me. It turned out that for eleven dollars between us we could get entry into all six national parks in South West Australia and climbing things was free.

We headed back to camp, after exploring the whole of the town and buying an ice lolly to cool down, to cook up some dinner. The boys cooked a sumptuous pasta dish (vegetarian much to Aaron's disgust) and I wrote some more of my blog. We met a nice bloke from Nuneaton who'd come down from where he lived in Perth for a few days with his wife and their son and daughter-in-law who had come over for a holiday from England. We had a good chat; he admired our van and gave us a few sight-seeing tips. He was a big walker and they loved the hill walks. We had a fire pit on our pitch and so we entertained ourselves for the evening hours by lighting a fire and keeping it going. The couple of bottles of wine managed to keep us amused in this task until bedtime. I only had a couple of glasses, but the boys celebrated our first night in Pemberton in style and I had the black eyes to prove it! When he got into bed, Aaron was trying to pull the covers up, which were stuck on something at the bottom of the bed, his hand slipped and he closed-fist punched me square in the left eye socket! It started to come up in a bruise instantly (I saw it when I went to brush my teeth), but the next day it turned purple and the other eye started darkening too. I just looked really, really tired in the photos!

The next morning, I awoke at sunrise with a throbbing head (from the punch) and a bit of confusion. It sounded as if hundreds of leaves were falling on the van, but it turned out to be raining. It was such a difference from the past few days because there was also a distinct chill left in the air from the night, when normally I woke up really hot as soon as the sun came up. We were supposed to be walking and climbing the tree, so it was a bit annoying. We had a bit of a lie-in, so that I could sleep off any potential concussion and the boys could avoid potential hangovers. We then got up, showered and had a hearty breakfast of egg sandwiches. By the time we left it was about eleven in the morning and the rain had eased off, but the Warren National Park, where the Bicentennial tree was, was only a few kilometres down the road. We drove into the forest, parked up near the tree and left our parking fee in the honesty box. I got about seven rungs up, shook like crazy, had my photo taken by the boys and scrambled back down. It seemed so unsafe because the rungs were quite far apart and there was nothing to stop you falling. It was then the boys' turn to show off by getting up to the first viewing platform –twenty-five metres up – with no problems. I took their photos then went to read all about the tree and the person it was named after; he was a pillar of the community who was still on several boards to help out his people. It was chosen as the Bicentennial tree to mark two hundred years since the founding of Australia. It would have been a small sapling at the time of the first English settlers and was chosen because of the spectacular views of sixty kilometres of forest scenery. Six people were allowed to climb at any one time and only four people were allowed in the two-tonne viewing cabin at the top of the tree. In high winds it could sway up to one point five metres in either direction. It was on reading this that the chap from Nuneaton said hello and I turned to see him and his family walking up to me. The men were venturing up, but the ladies kept me company in the panic yard. The boys hollered and waved to me from the very top and it made my knees wobble just looking up at them, so goodness knows how they did it. They got some great photos and videos, which demonstrated their nerves were a tad wobbly because the language was very colourful to say the least.

I had asked Mr Nuneaton's wife whether the 10.5km Warren Forest walk had very steep hills because the leaflet on it said that it did. They had just done it and she said I should be fine, even with a bad back, so we decided to try it. The first half of the walk was absolutely fabulous: great scenery, good company and lots of beautiful photographic opportunities. I was excited to find a large scorpion claw on the floor being carried off by hundreds of ants. I was also intrigued by huge ant hills, of which I had never seen such magnificent examples. At home they tend to be just holes in the floor, but in Australia they make majestic mountains in which to live. I could have stayed and watched them all day. When we reached the halfway mark of the circular route, however, we were faced with a hill. We started off and the extent of my unfitness was very quick to rear its ugly, out-of-breath head. I went very pink and my chest contracted. Aaron was a gentleman, though, and slowed his pace, carried my handbag for me and found me a walking stick, which stopped my back from hurting so much. It seemed that three point five of the final five kilometres were uphill and it was exhausting. I did get very excited about halfway up, though, because I found a skeleton by the side of the path. The small skull looked like it was probably a kangaroo and the leg bones looked like something out of a cartoon. It was a great advert for the efficiency of the eco-system because the bones were absolutely wiped clean and sparkling white. We also saw some huge ants, which had massive bums and very intimidating pincers at the front. They were about an inch long and the pincers looked as though they could easily pierce human skin. I was to find out later that they were called bull ants and are very nasty creatures, by which you wouldn't want to get bitten.

We were absolutely thrilled to finish the walk back at the tree and the van was very welcoming. Although we had a late breakfast at about 10am, it was then 4pm and we were famished. We stopped at the supermarket on the way home, and I cooked us some chicken fried rice for dinner. We then lit the fire as it got very dark very quickly and pretty early. We were excited to try toasting marshmallows on skewers and they were absolutely delicious; crispy and caramelised on the outside and melty and sweet on the inside. They were so sickly, though, that I only managed four before I felt a bit sick. I called my second cousin's wife, Kim, as we were to be going to see her at her vineyard in Mount Barker a couple of days later.

Walpole, Denmark and Mount Barker: 16/12/2009

We left Pemberton early in the morning on what was quite a cloudy and cool day. On our way to Denmark, we planned to stop at the Valley of the Giants in Walpole to do the walk in the tree canopies. The Pemberton campsite receptionist gave me a flyer so that we knew how to get there. Again, it was only one road. On the reverse of the flyer it advertised the "Giant Tingle Tree", so we decided to stop there too as it was on the way. It was a great day to drive weather-wise because the breeze kept us nice and cool. In fact, for the long trek the day before and the Walpole activities, I had long trousers on and Walpole even required a fleece! It was a stark contrast to the heat of Perth and Margaret River.

We turned at the signs for the Giant Tingle Tree and our tired van gave shudders of protest as we made our slow progress along the red dirt track for four kilometres. I read that the tingle trees are some of the largest in the whole world, but can only be found in Walpole in WA. As we unfurled our aching limbs from the van in the car park, we filled with dread at the prospect of another long walk because the trek from the day before had taken its toll on all of us, not just on my dodgy joints. We were all very grateful when we discovered it was only a 400m walk and the slope wasn't at an evil gradient. The trees were spectacular. Although they weren't as tall as the Bicentennial tree that the boys had scaled the previous day (most were a mere 40m high compared with the 75m Bicentennial tree), their trunks certainly had more girth to write home about. A lot of the older trees had large buttress roots, a few of which formed small caves beneath them, which inspired thoughts of pixies and fairies making their homes there. The whole forest seemed to have a very fairy-tale-like quality to it. When the famed Giant Tingle Tree loomed in front of us, we could see how it acquired its title. A van that called itself home for six backpackers (how their beast made it up the hills of South WA with six people, their luggage and their booze, I'll never know!) had pulled up before us and an Irish lass asked Adam to take their picture in the living-room sized space in its buttress roots. To demonstrate its size, they all held hands and two of them touched the inside of the trunk; there was still room for a couple of extra people in the chain because they certainly weren't tightly packed. Goodness knows how many clowns you could get in there!

On leaving the Giant Tingle Tree, we most definitely weren't tempted by the 10km forest walk back to the town of Walpole and opted for the less ambitious 300 metres back to our van. It was a shorter dirt track to reach the highway (the tree is on a one-way dirt track loop) and we were soon happily on our way to walk in the canopy of the tingle tree forest. We paid the entrance fee that allowed us on the canopy walk plus the forest floor walk through the older tingle trees called "the ancient walk" and the small nature museum. We did the canopy walk first so as not to allow me time to get worried about the heights. The suspended bridge started wide and low, but soon got up to the full 40m height of the canopy and became very narrow. I kept a lid on my anxiety apart from shouting at the boys who thought it was very funny to sway the already unstable walkway and jump up and down on it. I was able to enjoy the spectacular views, take lots of photos and look all around me (except up). I was, however, more than happy to get back to solid ground. The problem was that the walkway was a metal grate, through which you could see right down to the forest floor, which was a very long way down.

When we emerged back into the open-air lobby area, we heard someone say, "Oh, hello there," and were surprised to see Mr Nuneaton and his family there. We all had a good natter and the ladies apologised profusely to me for saying that the nature walk wasn't steep. They said that they only had the small section to go when they saw us and panicked when they realised how wrong they were. They said that they had hoped that we hadn't gone that far or I would have hated them! I laughed and told a little white lie by saying I was absolutely fine, refraining from saying how I had been cursing their names when every blind corner revealed an even longer, steeper slope to mountaineer! They were just about to tackle the very short canopy walk and we went off to do the ancient one. The difference between the two sets of trees was quite obvious. The older ones had much girthier trunks and much more pronounced and cavernous buttress roots. After hauling myself rather un-lady-likely over a fallen tree and up over a handrail to take the short cut that the boys found (there are only so many trees of the like that you can "ooh" and "ahh" at when you ache like we did), it was only the small museum to whizz around to get our money's worth. It was here that I learnt about the scary bull ants we'd seen with the large pincers and bulbous bottoms. I also saw a stuffed version of the animal that I had seen squished on the side of the road, which I had commented that it looked like a baby leopard. It was actually called the rather disappointingly general title of "feral cat". Not quite as exciting as some of the names of other native mammals, such as the large rodent-like "quokka", which is very rare but found in that part of Australia. Sadly – but quite predictably given their numbers – we did not happen to see any of those.

On leaving, we once again saw Mr Nuneaton. We had a short chat, said the clichéd, 'Oh we must stop meeting like this,' and wished each other bon voyage. With that, we were on our way to Denmark. The cheapest campsite was called the River Mouth campsite, so it was here that we planned to stay for the next two nights. The entrance was along the river and we found that swimming alongside us were magnificently odd-looking pelicans. For such strange bucket-mouthed creatures, they certainly swim majestically. The receptionist was very friendly and gave us a couple of maps, showing the boys a couple of good fishing spots. After Adam had kicked all the kangaroo poo from our pitch and we had set up the tent in record time (for we were now experts), we headed into town to explore. I found an internet café to upload my previous blogs while the boys bought some fishing bait to go with the cheap rods that we had found in Walpole: the boys bought blue ones and I got a pink one – it was so pretty! We then went to one of the recommended spots, which was at the top of a steeply inclined dirt track, much to the disgust of the van. I got out to explore and take some photos of the beautiful scenery before retreating back to the van to read (and, as it turned out, have a snooze) because I ached too much to fish and it was very cold and windy up there. The boys had fun, although they didn't manage to catch us dinner as promised. Aaron caught a small red rock cod (which apparently aren't good table fish anyway) and Adam caught a very pretty little bream with fins edged in beautiful light petrol blue.

We were all shattered from the strenuous last few days, so we had all fallen asleep by about 10pm. This meant that we were very early to rise the next day and pottered around sorting breakfast and getting ready for the Mount Barker trip. I gave my second cousin's wife Kim a call to say that we were leaving at about 10.30am, but stupidly forgot to ask for a reminder of the directions as it had now been a week since I had looked them up on Google Maps and had mislaid them. Consequently, after stopping for a bunch of flowers, this resulted in me making a wrong turn and ending up at the beginning of the town when I knew that their road was just outside Mount Barker. An embarrassingly sheepish call later and we found their vineyard easily and were soon sitting with a glass (a very small one for me as I was driving) of their tantalisingly refreshing Sauvignon Blanc and updating Kim on our adventures since we had last seen them several moons before. She was a fabulous hostess and more than made up for the absence of Tom, who was at work in Perth, and Clea, their daughter and winemaker who was teaching, which she did two days a week. She put on a fabulous spread with bread, crackers, sumptuous cheeses, olives, antipasto and delicious dips of hummus, salmon mousse and pate. Just when we thought that we couldn't eat any more, she made us an offer we couldn't refuse: homemade choc chip muffins. All this and she kept apologising for the lack of hostessing because she had run out of time to prepare properly! I wondered just how much more she could have done because she kept two very large boys and me, with the appetite of a horse after having been on such a long course of steroids, extremely satisfied.

After letting our lunch go down and chatting about travelling and the vineyard, Kim took us behind the scenes; something the Maggie River wine tour lacked. We saw the two huge aluminium vats for the whites and the splendid oak barrels for the reds. She had explained how ten years ago Clea had had the idea of setting up the vineyard and winery. She had done the viticulture course and acquired many wine-related friends and acquaintances during her wine-making apprenticeship. This resulted in the acquisition of the precious cuttings from which the magnificent acres of vines seen that day would grow. She showed Tom and Kim how to plant the mere sticks in the ground and between them they planted four wines: Chenin Blanc, Sauvignon Blanc, Cabernet Sauvignon and Shiraz. The small production meant that they could describe themselves charmingly as a "boutique" winery. Kim laughed when she reminisced about Tom's scepticism, saying to Clea, 'What have you talked us into?!' and repeating the phrase, 'They'll never grow!' Kim took great mirth when they had grapes and wine coming out of their ears and she could remind Tom of their humble beginnings.

We had a look at the beautifully green vines and the tiny, polka-dot grapes. We tried without success to find the racehorse iguana that Buster the handyman had found had taken up residence under one of the bridges, much to Kim's annoyance as it frightened her. We also fought the flies, swallowing a couple, to visit their home that they had built at the other end of the vineyard. It was a stunning, open-plan building that offered a great haven from the heat and the flies that had crept up on us during the previously cloudy day. She also showed us where they had had a fire in the February of that year. It wiped out the old oak tree, which had housed their grandson's magnificent tree house, and it reached the corner of the winery. Luckily, their son-in-law drove the local fire engine that resided on their land (it was a beauty) and so it was out before it reached the vines or the house, but it still caused a lot of damage. Kim described how frightening it was when it looked as though they could lose their home and livelihood, but the sudden changes in wind direction actually worked in their favour. It was a harrowing thought that something as small as a spark from a thresher, which was the cause of the fire, could threaten so much. Thank goodness Tom and his family now employ a drop and run philosophy because a lot of deaths in Victoria that year were caused by the futile stay and protect stance. As we saw first-hand in Thailand post-tsunami, your loved ones are your most precious possession and anything else can be rebuilt.

The boys wanted to get some fishing in before the day was out and we didn't want to impose on Kim for too long as they were in the process of finishing up at the winery to return to Perth for Christmas, so we said our goodbyes when we got back later. Her daughter and son-in-law were to go off bush-camping for the holidays, so Tom and Kim thought they'd celebrate their first Christmas without the grandkids at their home in the city. She sent us off with a bottle of sauvignon blanc and a shiraz that we planned to save for Christmas Day and we headed off feeling like we'd only been there an hour. It turned out that we had actually been there for three hours, which showed just how great our visit was.

Back in Denmark, we picked up some tackle and headed to the river where there were signs up saying that pink snapper could be fished there. The boys fished and I sunbathed on the grassy bank as it was gorgeous weather.

We had to plaster ourselves in insect repellent as there were ghastly sand flies about. These were the size of blue bottles, but had a mosquito-like mouth that was huge and very painful when it bit, as I unfortunately experienced. As it got dark, we returned to the campsite and cooked homemade beefburgers on the camp kitchen's gas barbeques (we were not allowed our own barbeque due to the high fire risk) and the boys headed for a pint in the local pub while I enjoyed some personal space to read my book in peace and quiet. It was then another early night before the drive to Albany in the morning. It had been another very busy, but highly enjoyable few days.

Nullarboor

After travelling through Esperance, it was time to start the dreaded drive across the Nullarbor desert plains. We planned a 940km drive to stay overnight at Border Village, which is fifty metres inside the South Australian border. We were all pretty tired because the trains on the rail line were directly behind all of our heads, so we got woken up by their fog horns every couple of hours. Why they need to do this at 5am, I will never know. I did the first five-hour drive because Adam was definitely not a morning person, and I got a lot more tired in the afternoons because of my arthritis and the medication. We had been warned that the Nullarbor drive is the most boring drive we would ever do, but I didn't find I agreed. The scenery was a lot greener –

with trees and shrubs lining the road – than I had expected, and it changed quite frequently; we were even alongside the Southern Sea for a large portion, but sadly we were in the wrong season for whale watching. I got excited when I passed the sign that said we were starting the longest straight stretch of road in the world at ninety miles. It was impressive and I took photos of the road disappearing off the edge of the horizon. We swapped over and Adam was tickled at Aaron and my alternate head bobbing as we were falling asleep. I was shattered! It was hard work driving in such gusty wind. It was blowing in from the south, so it was very chilly because it was effectively blowing in from the Antarctic, which was a nice relief from the heat of the desert, but made driving pretty challenging. We passed some very amusing town names like "Grass Patch" and "Salmon Gums".

After a gruelling, yet fun ten hours, we arrived at Border Village and checked in at the campsite reception, which was inside the BP Garage. We trundled around the back past the giant fibreglass kangaroo and pulled up to our powered site. There didn't seem to be an edge to the campsite, which made me a little uneasy. This was not helped by the sign on the toilet door, which said, "Please keep the door closed, it is for your own convenience", and had a picture of a brown snake on it. We set up camp and went for a swim, which counted as our showers seeing as you had to pay two dollars for only ten minutes in the grubby showers. We went to the pub next door and had a drink or two and a good meal, then headed to bed for an early night.

We awoke at 5am to leave at half past. Adam was thoroughly miserable because he'd had no sleep. It had rained in the night and we had failed to set up the tent properly and he got wet. Things got worse as he had to lie holding the sides of the tent up to protect it from the gales that had whipped up. Aaron and I were no happier because neither of us had got much sleep either. I had been afraid of having a night terror because Adam had stamped on a massive hairy spider. Also, every time we switched off the light, we could hear the dreaded whine of a mosquito. I killed two on the curtain and four on the roof, but there was one that would not show itself no matter how many times we switched on the light to try and hunt the little bugger. Luckily, I was not massively tasty to mozzies (probably the amount of drugs in my blood), but Aaron was obviously a tasty treat because they even went through the oil slick of insect repellent to bite him. So, I was a bit apprehensive starting the second leg of the Nullarbor with such a lack of sleep, but a caffeine boost was all I needed and I was fine. Adam slept in the back for the first few hours of my drive, but was rudely awoken when we pulled in to get petrol and the wave of heat hit us as the clouds finally cleared. This was the beginning of the worst drive of my whole life. We filled up the tank with the pricey desert petrol (the most expensive was 171 cents per litre, which was still cheap as chips compared to England, but a bit of a shock compared with the west of the country) and got something to nibble. When we got back in, Adam could no longer sleep because the back of the van was like a kiln. It was better to keep the passenger window wound up because the gale-force winds were now coming from the desert to the north and it was like having a hurricane-strength hot hairdryer on your face. We all sweated profusely and it made us feel really quite ill. I felt like I had heat stroke by the time we reached the magnificent scenery of the Flinders Ranges and found it quite difficult to appreciate them. We didn't see much wildlife on the second leg because a lot of the road there was fenced off. This meant that there weren't as many dead roos or crows feasting on them. I did see a spectacular bird, which my mum was to later help me identify as a wedge-tailed eagle. It was golden and looked like a cross between a buzzard and an eagle. It was the biggest bird I had ever seen in the wild and it didn't move an inch from its kangaroo carcass as we drove past, but gave us a death stare that sent shivers down my spine. I cheered up when I saw the sign for the town of "Iron Knob", though, as I have the sense of humour of a thirteen-year-old boy sometimes, and Adam slowed down for me to take a picture!

We had never been more grateful to see a campsite sign. We checked in for the night in the Port Augusta campsite, bought a bag of ice to cool the warm Esky and ran to the pool, which was lovely and icy cold. I was sure you could see steam as Aaron and I got in. Adam was checking in with his parents to reassure them that we hadn't gone missing on the Nullarbor and the desert drive was now over. We met a guy from New Zealand who was swimming with his kids and had a good old natter with him. He gave us some great pointers for the Kiwi leg of our trip in January. They had spent nearly two weeks driving from the north down to the south coast of Australia via Uluru and he said it was torture! We found out that night that it had reached forty-six degrees Celsius where we were driving and it was hotter inside the van – no wonder we felt like we were being cooked in our own juices and were leaving people-shaped sweat patches on the seats! We all got an early night once again, but were grateful that we could have a leisurely time getting up in the morning as the drive to Adelaide would only take three and a half hours. I was amused to look through my photos to see that I had done well in capturing the giant fibreglass sculptures that the Aussies are so proud of. I got a kangaroo, a cockatoo and a whale.

Adelaide: Christmas Eve 2009

We actually checked out of the Port Augusta campsite an hour late because we hadn't changed the time according to the time difference properly. At least it meant we had a good lie in, although I'd had yet another terrible night's sleep because of the heat. I did the first stint of driving of just over an hour and a half and we swapped halfway through. The drive was relatively uneventful and we were happy to see signs to the city as it had been a while since we were in an actual city. We stopped at the big supermarket to get Christmas dinner and booze for the following day, then headed to the campsite to check in. We bought a new airbed for Adam because the other one had punctured in several places and the sites were concrete, so definitely not practical for the bed rolls. I was very grateful that he'd graciously offered to sleep in the tent during this leg of our travels, meaning I could sleep on the bed in the van to try and limit the damage to my back. He is a wonderful friend, and I don't think I've ever thanked him properly for that!

We set up camp, had some two-minute noodles for dinner (mmm… nutritious!) and, surprise surprise, headed to the pub for a drink. It was a shock to find the alcohol was about half the price of Perth and it made us realise we were no longer in WA. One drink turned into three or four and a pizza. We all headed home when we realised just how tired we were. I was excited to see a possum in the trees behind our van; in fact, there were two and they were very cute. I managed to get a picture with my night option on my camera.

Unfortunately, after a very good evening and the excitement of the wildlife, I had a very uncomfortable night because I had to get up three times and run to the toilet block. I was very sick with a nasty tummy bug, which obviously wasn't helped by the red wine I had drunk. This continued the next day and I was unable to participate in the massive full English fry up we had planned to barbeque on Christmas morning. It was a long time until I had stopped being sick long enough to eat a couple of crackers, and I missed out on any of the Christmas alcohol we had invested in. The boys said that they wouldn't touch the Trapper's Gully wine from my second cousin's vineyard and would just drink the boxes of red and port that we had bought. I was sure four point four litres of wine plus two litres of port and a bottle of whiskey would do them and I was right!

Late morning, we all went for a swim in the pretty little campsite pool. I was determined to be festive and so donned my Santa boxer shorts over my bikini and wore my Santa hat, which I didn't even take off when I was swimming. It was the strangest feeling being in an outdoor swimming pool on Christmas Day. Although it was fun, I was incredibly homesick as I wanted to be wrapped up and snugly by the fire with my family. It just didn't feel like Christmas and I started to get a bit sad, especially because it hadn't been that long since my mum had got the all-clear from cancer and she was spending Christmas on her own. But, after a stern word with myself and my tummy having calmed down, I relaxed and could enjoy the day for what it was – another beautiful day in the Aussie sunshine.

Christmas dinner was a bit of a mission with no camp kitchen and only a two-ring camp stove, but Aaron and I pulled it off; more Aaron than me, actually, I just did the stuffing! We had turkey steaks, roast potatoes with onions, broccoli, carrot and swede mash, stuffing balls and lashings of gravy. It was delicious! The crackers that I bought from the equivalent of Poundland showed exactly their worth. We were happy with the hats, but even though they had kittens on the side of the crackers, the stickers inside had a picture of a dog with a Christmas hat – it was as though they were saying "screw you, cat lovers, you're stuck with a dog"! Adam read his joke out: What is the difference between lightning and electricity? You don't have to pay for electricity. I know cracker jokes are notoriously bad, but that didn't even seem like a joke. It was more like a bad translation from a foreign statement. The funny side of it, though, was when Aaron and I read our jokes they were all identical. It turned out that the stickers and the jokes were all the same in each cracker. I think we got our three dollars' worth.

While cooking the feast, something a little déjà vu-like happened. Who should rock up (there's another Aussie phrase for you), but the South Africans we'd met at an earlier stop! We gave our season's greetings and they set about sorting their tent out on the pitch next to us. They managed to find some big rocks from somewhere and used these to tie their guy ropes to because the pitches were concrete. After cheese, crackers and mince pies, Hendrick (the son of the duo) came to join us for some port and we had a good old chat. He was really nice and he told us a bit about South Africa and his travels with his dad. We got told off for making too much noise because it had gone 11pm. I went to bed hoping to feel better in the morning.

In fact, I did feel a lot better, and got up to go for a swim in the freezing cold pool. Adam cooked me my fry-up on the camp barbeque and the boys had eggs and beans on toast for brunch. I was still shattered from the bug and the boys felt a bit rough, so we lounged by the pool for the morning. Sunny, our van, was very grateful for the rest after the Nullarbor. In the afternoon, we went to explore the city. It seemed smaller than Perth, but it was a lot prettier.

The architecture was fantastic, and I was impressed with most of the university buildings. I was sad that I didn't get to go to the zoo because they'd just got a pair of pandas and I couldn't recall ever seeing them before. It was incredibly expensive, though, and I was saving myself for Sydney Zoo as it is one of (if not) the biggest zoos in the world and was Steve Irwin's haunt. We had a good walk around and took a few photos. Adelaide seemed to have a lot of statues and sculptures, some of which were very quirky. I particularly liked the pig sculptures that they had around the bins in the centre – that's one way to encourage you to deposit your litter there!

That evening, after we had explored for a while, we found the restaurant district. We had decided to spend my mother's Christmas money on a nice meal in a restaurant because it had been yonks since we went to a nice restaurant all together. We found a steak and seafood restaurant, which was absolutely lovely, called Daniel's. I had bruschetta to start, then the seafood platter, which consisted of huge prawns, two types of fish, scallops and calamari. It was fabulous, so thank you very much, Ma -- you gave us a fantastic Boxing Day! When we got back to the campsite after a lovely stroll along the river feeling way too full, we went to the cheap local with our new South African friend, Hendrick. I was driving early in the morning and still wasn't on top form, so wasn't drinking. I was also very tired, so Aaron took me home and we were asleep by 11.15pm. Adam, on the other hand, staggered home at 2am – good job I was driving to Horsham, which was our one-night stop-off on the way to Melbourne. He had a great time, though, and that's all that matters.

Melbourne: 28/12/2009

The journey to Melbourne was very pleasant apart from gear troubles. We took the coastal road and it was winding, hilly and beautifully picturesque, but Sunny the van was not happy. In fact, at the top of one hill when we had passed the Goulbern wineries, she gave a little splutter having struggled immensely and was no longer willing to go into fourth gear at all. It was a bit of a blow after all the new stuff we had given her, a brand new radiator and starter motor within the last few weeks. It was going to make life very difficult when we were planning to sell her in the near future.

The next day was dedicated to trying to sort out the van and get it up on some websites to try and sell her in Sydney. I called round a few mechanics and they gave me quotes that we couldn't afford, but it didn't make any difference anyway because they were all shut/booked up for the holidays until after we were due to fly out of Sydney. One really nice bloke recommended to me that we put it up for sale as normal, for about $4000 and then when someone test drove it explain how much it would cost to fix, why we couldn't do it because of the time of year and knock down the price so that they could afford to buy the van and fix her up. I did just that and got a call from a nice German girl, but she finished reading the advert whilst talking to me and apologised that they were in Brisbane and wanted the van in order to get to Sydney! It was a promising sign, though.

For our sightseeing in Melbourne, I was delighted to discover that there was a free bus that went in a loop around the important landmarks of the city while a recorded tour guide told us what we were seeing. I'd been struggling so much with lots of walking, so this was music to my ears. Aaron and I headed into the city, and our priority was to get something to eat. We then headed to Myer, which was an important department store for me. You see, just before we left Perth, Aaron and Adam had seen a programme about a lady that had made $3million despite the recession and was the only woman in Australia to do so. She had invented a soap to cure eczema and psoriasis, which was only available in Myer stores, but was supposed to be a miracle cure. She discovered that her son, who was covered top to toe in eczema, responded fantastically to her goat Billy's milk when she bathed him in it and so made soap from it. After a while searching and eventually resorting to asking an assistant, we found it. It was called Billie-goat Soap and I was excited because it was very affordable. Simple things please simple minds, as the saying goes. I got the milk and honey one in case the other ones smelt too much like goats and it was lovely. I was very much hoping it would soothe my red raw psoriasis.

After a full day of sightseeing, we returned to the campsite. I quickly got changed and headed straight to the pool while Aaron had a nap in the van. Adam was in the pool and said that he had fully intended to join us, but was too hot, so stayed by the pool!

New Year's Eve 2009

I had planned to go to the market the next morning, but the boys advised against it. They said that yet more walking would make me more swollen than I already was from the long drives and copious number of steps and I should also get a lie in because it would be a very late night for New Year's Eve. Although I didn't say so, I knew they were probably right and said that I'd see, but didn't set my alarm for the morning. I was disappointed, but thought I'd better prioritise the celebrations with my boys. Due to the fantastic weather, Adam and I spent the day by the lovely pool. Aaron is not a sun lover and so hid away in the shade of the van playing on Adam's PSP. It was very pleasant because every time the wind dropped and we felt too hot, we could just dip in the extremely chilly pool and instantly cool down. There was also a hot tub, which was a bit odd in the sunshine, so we didn't use that very much. I left in the afternoon to try and spruce myself up for the evening. I had a shower, straightened my hair and put on makeup for the first time in ages, but the foundation didn't last very long in the heat – particularly because the campsite hairdryer made me even hotter! Still, it lasted long enough for a few photos at the beginning of the evening. We had planned to use the gas barbeque (most campsites and most parks in Australia provide these for free to encourage you to not use your own to lower the bushfire risk) near our pitch to cook our dinner, but there were three guys and a girl using it. It looked like they had finished, so we asked them if we were free to use it and they said we were. They stayed while we cooked and ate our dinner and we all got chatting. They were a couple from Scotland called Jen and Dave and two guys from Taiwan with whom they had met in Darwin called Derek and Levi, which were names that they had chosen to use instead of their Taiwanese names for Aussies and Europeans because nobody could pronounce their real names!

The boys and I had the bottle of white and red from Tom and Kim to start off our drinking on a delicious note. This wine was an absolute delight and I was very happy that we could indulge in such palatable wine on such a day. So, thank you very much to you, Tom and Kim. Then when our taste buds were more impaired, we could brave the cheapo box of red filth. We all started drinking together and got on like a house on fire. So much so, we completely lost track of time. Another guy from England joined us because he was on his own (his mate had a girlfriend back home and abandoned him to go back to her partway through the trip) and introduced us to Bundaberg rum, otherwise known as Bundi. This is an exceedingly popular spirit in Australia and it is actually more palatable than I had been told. I only had a sip, but the boys went a bit mad and were downing it straight. Another couple of Aussie guys joined us whom we'd met on previous nights in the ping pong room, and we decided to head into town. We had initially meant to leave for the tram at around 9pm, having drunk enough to make the city-wide alcohol-free zone not matter, but ended up leaving shortly before 11pm! Fortunately, all public transport was free after 6pm on New Year's Eve and ran all night. It is such a good idea to combat drink driving. By this time, we had witnessed an awe-inspiring display of lightning and the heavens had opened to drench us to the skin. Jen's and my hair had gone a bit wild because we'd got caught in the downpour halfway back from the toilet block. Our makeup was also streaked down our faces, but by that point we were having such a giggle that we really didn't care. The plan was to head to Federation Square where we had seen them setting up the entertainment stage the previous day. This was supposed to be a hotspot for seeing the fireworks, which were planned differently this year. Normally they were set off from Yarra River, but this year the skyscrapers were all rigged with them from their rooftops so that they would be visible from any point in the city. It was still pouring with rain and we wondered whether they would still go ahead with the fireworks.

On the way to the square, everyone we passed was very jovial and we were incredibly excited about the night ahead. Aaron, Jen, Dave, Derek and I all arrived at a great spot in the square to see the big screen where they were showing the African singers and dancers who were putting on a great show on the stage. We had a great view. We then realised, however, that we had lost absolutely everyone else, but with only fifteen minutes before midnight because we had cut it so fine, it was too late to look for them. There was an old bloke standing next to Aaron and I wearing a flasher's mac. He asked us if we were poms and, upon discovering that we were, opened his mac (luckily fully dressed underneath) to reveal loads of secret pockets containing cans of Carlton Draught beer. He gave one to each of us and we toasted the evening as well as getting photos to prove his creepiness! I checked that they were unopened when I received mine and subtly gave the area with the ring pull a good wipe with my top. The guys on stage then started getting very excited and the countdown began. The dense crowd jumped up and down as one and screamed with delight. On the stroke of midnight, all the couples had passionate kisses, then everyone started hugging and kissing one another, wishing each other Happy New Year, whether they were strangers or not. It was joyous and I felt elated. I quickly texted my mum and immediately turned to Aaron worrying that I had just sent her the soppiest message in the world, but couldn't quite remember what I'd said! Everyone started leaving the square, so we set about trying to find everyone else and headed for the tram home. By this point it was 2.30am and we still hadn't found the others. Aaron started getting worried on the tram and I tried calling and texting Adam, as I had been since we realised that they were missing, but he still didn't answer. When we got back to the site, we found Adam passed out in his tent! It had been a fantastic night, if a bit eventful at the end, but had been the best New Year celebrations I had ever experienced, and I have not had one as good since!

It was still raining the next day and we were sad to find that we had left all our towels to get drenched and very muddy in the rain, so I had to shower with my pool towel. It was better than nothing. Aaron was exceedingly hungover and Adam was very sheepish. It turned out that when we got to Federation Square, he immediately lost us. Instead of doing the sensible thing and phoning to see where we were, his drunken mind went into automatic pilot telling him he was somewhere strange, and he had to get to familiar ground. So, with the Aussie brothers and Levi the Taiwanese guy, he spent midnight in a taxi back to the campsite and didn't remember anything from leaving the campsite to getting back there! He was very disappointed, especially when he saw how much fun was had from looking at our crazy photos. I suppose one of the benefits of being on medication was that I had to be so careful with what I drank. Having been drinking nothing for so long, the couple of glasses of wine and the can of beer I'd had went straight to my head but didn't leave me hungover. The issue for me, though, was that I'd been on my feet for so long, plus I'd been dancing like a crazy person because the alcohol and the adrenaline of the partying had dulled my pain for the evening. After a day recovering, I called my mum to wish her a Happy New Year and find out what my text to her had said. She said that I said I was having "the best effing New Year's of my life" and I was utterly horrified at my language to her, until she said that I genuinely wrote "effing" and not the actual expletive! I was very glad that I could even censor myself when tipsy because I had been trying to curb my bad language, it having deteriorated since working with Aussies who like to curse!

So that was Melbourne. Fabulous architecture, laid back attitude and the best New Year's Eve I have ever had. I would definitely like to return some day and perhaps see the new pandas that the zoo had acquired.

Canberra? Wagga Wagga and Sydney: 02/01/2010

We got up to pack the stuff away ready to drive to Canberra. We had planned to spend one night there to see the architecture, as we were told that there is apparently not much else to do in this city, on our way to Sydney. I started off the journey with a two-and-a-half-hour drive and stopped just before the border into the Australian Capital Territory before Adam took over. It was a very pleasant drive through a pretty green and hilly landscape. We were successfully avoiding fourth gear, but strife hit when we were three quarters of the way to Canberra. Sunny started making horrible clunking, grinding noises every time Adam touched the accelerator, so we pulled over to take a look. The oil light hadn't come on, but it was pretty low, so we topped her up. We let her rest then tried starting her again while looking at the engine to try and see the problem. The noise was still there, so Adam called Leon, our mechanic from Perth, to ask his advice. He asked to listen to the noise and when he did, said, 'Sounds like she's about to blow, mate.' He said to let her cool down, then top up the coolant and hope for the best. We did as he said, but sadly he was a very good mechanic and was right with his first instinct about the noise because there was an almighty bang and something shot out of the bottom. He could start a new line of work as an audio-mechanic!

She refused to start again and we were forced to resign ourselves to the fact that that was the end of our drive because she was gone. We had to call a tow truck that took us to the nearest town of Wagga Wagga, which was about twenty minutes away. Fortunately, he was an absolute diamond and helped us out a lot. His girlfriend Kathy came and picked up Adam because he only had two spare seats in his truck. He towed us to a campsite where we arranged to stay for the night. I had to get to Sydney the next day because the morning after that was my all-important rheumatology appointment where I was to get my six-month supply of injections. Kathy said that she would pick Aaron and I up the next morning (the boys wouldn't let me go on my own, despite my protests!) and take us to the bus to Sydney, which we booked that night. John the tow-truck guy would then pick Adam up on Monday morning, take him to Cash Convertors to sell all the sellable contents of the van, take him to the wrecker's yard to scrap the van and then take him to the bus station. He did all this for the flat fee of 300 dollars, which is what it would have cost in pounds back in the UK just for the initial tow. They were both more than helpful and we were all very grateful to them.

Aaron and I were packing well after it got dark, trying to

sort out the essentials, as we had to go back to backpacking sooner than we thought. We all called home and explained the situation. Aaron and I were in trouble because of how much had gone wrong since landing in Australia and there were a few moments when we thought we would have to cut our losses and give up on the rest of the trip. Thankfully, our parents came to the rescue, so here is a very sincere and special thank you to Viv and Joe (my mum and dad), and Dawn and Graham (Aaron's mum and dad), who helped us realise that this was a once-in-a-lifetime opportunity and helped us out with the means to continue with Adam to try and finish the journey we had started together. We managed to get a few hours' sleep and then were up early to finish packing and head to the bus station. The Greyhound coach was actually very nice and Aaron had enough leg room as long as the person in front of him kept their seat upright. Luckily that seat was empty for the most part, so he was okay.

In Melbourne, we had taken advantage of a closing down camping store and bought a plush three-man (Adam and Aaron size man) tent for an absolute pittance, which would save us a fortune on hostel costs for the rest of our Australian leg and in New Zealand because it would mean we could stay in cheap campsites or, at a push, the beach! I had booked us a campsite for the night with a late check-in. We arrived at the bus/train station just after 9pm after a seven-hour journey. We got the train to a suburb called Miranda,– and don't worry, I won't repeat the many puns about entering Miranda (oops!). From here, it was a fifteen-minute walk to the campsite, but we were struck with a problem. The printed Google directions (the app wasn't around back then), in their infinite wisdom, said, "head north on Kia Ora Road when leaving the station". There was only one exit from the station, so why on earth they couldn't have said "turn right", I'll never know. With no stars with which to navigate (as if we'd have known how to use them anyway!), and no compass, we were stumped as to which direction was north. At the moment we were trying to figure out where we could find a taxi, a voice behind us shouted, 'Are you lost?' in an Aussie accent. It was a girl of about our age standing in the open door of her car. We said we were heading to the Sydney Tourist Park and knew it was pretty much on that road, but didn't know which direction. She said she knew it and to jump in. The friend she was picking up wasn't arriving for half an hour and it wasn't even five minutes down the road. We gratefully accepted, stuffed in our bags and then folded ourselves into the smallest car in the world! Thank goodness it was so close. She said she had just got back from travelling around South America and said she knew what it was like to get favours from strangers and was happy to give something back. We thanked her profusely and got out of the car just as it started to rain; bloody typical! We eventually found the office in the middle of the very shabby-looking caravan park and I gave the owner a call. He told us what site we were on and we used the map on the office window to find it. We then went back to the relative shelter of the door overhang on the office where we could use the light to set up the new tent for the first time, whilst trying to keep as much rain off it as possible. This wasn't as difficult as we feared, and we were then able to carry it over to the pitch. We blew up the airbed, got ready for bed and crashed out.

We were woken at dawn by a cacophony of birds. The tent was not in the slightest bit soundproof, unlike the van, and the white cockatoos and magpies were particularly noisy. Sadly, the campsite failed to improve in the daylight. It was a bit of a hole compared with the relative luxury of the majority of campsites we had been fortunate enough to stay in up to that point. However, all the nicer campsites were fully booked thanks to it being school summer holidays, so we were stuck there for the whole week. I headed to the office to pay for the week (unfortunately it was no cheaper than the nice ones) and asked him to put my medication in his fridge. There were three men's toilets and three women's in a prefab block that looked like my old primary school's mobiles. The rooms had a toilet and a shower each, so when I was desperate for the toilet in the morning, I was forced to hold it because the showers were all in use. This was making me late for my appointment and I was getting extremely nervous. I kept telling myself, 'As long as I make my appointment, all will be fine.' After getting extremely annoyed that someone was blow-drying her hair for fifteen minutes, I was finally able to get ready and rushed Aaron to the station as he said he'd come with me.

My appointment was in a suburb called Kogarah (pronounced cog-ra), which was on the way into the city on the trainline we'd used the previous night. We checked out the map at the station and were relieved to see that it was nearby. I filled out the forms when we arrived and waited for the doctor. Aaron and I were then invited into his office and we began the appointment. My heart stopped pounding when he said he would be happy to do the prescription because the examination showed I had done very well on the Humira. He asked when I was leaving and a look of horror came on his face when we told him it was in a week. He said he'd call the office that he needed to send the prescription to for approval to find out whether they'd let him fax it to them. More and more issues arose and my heart sank lower and lower. It turned out that despite saying I could get six months' supply, my Perth doctor was ill informed. They wouldn't even look at me until three months from the first injection was completed, which would be 26th January. Even then, they wouldn't give me six months' supply because I was leaving to return to the UK. They wouldn't give me anything and as it dawned on me that this was yet another hurdle that I'd crashed into I couldn't hold back my quivering lip or tears any longer. The doctor offered me several tissues and kept apologising, which made me feel even worse because it wasn't his fault and he was lovely. He put me back on the full whack of methotrexate to complement the Humira, which meant zero alcohol again and expensive blood tests in one of the subsequent countries. This was annoying because in Australia I got them free on Medicare. At least I had enough injections to get me back to the UK and, together with the tablets, I was hoping to find carrying my backpack a lot easier. I didn't actually risk having a blood test in any of the subsequent countries. I felt it was less of a risk to wait the few weeks left of our travels to get home.

Aaron and I left the rheumatologist feeling very low. Despite feeling like I'd come away from the doctor with nothing, I still had to pay the whopping $230 initial consultation fee and that stung. Aaron said he was considering becoming a pessimist as it would have been a lot less painful. I could see on his face how worried he was for me and this was very upsetting. To cheer ourselves up, we found a nice Greek café and had a lovely brunch. We then decided to head to the cinema in the city because the weather was still very grey and we didn't want to sight-see too much without Adam. We looked at the map and found a place called Cinema City on George Street in the centre. We started off down that road and found it turned into a road called Broadway. Before we realised, we'd walked miles in the wrong direction! Luckily, the day tripper tickets we'd bought included all buses and ferries, so we hopped on a bus and got off when we saw a big cinema sign. We looked everywhere in the shopping complex and saw signs everywhere advertising a cinema on level three, but couldn't find it and felt a little crazy. We eventually asked the lady at the information desk only to be told that the cinema had closed down. Why didn't they remove or at least cover the signs, then? Luckily, she told us there was a cinema only five minutes down the road. We decided to watch *Sherlock Holmes* with Robert Downey Jr. We spent a couple of extra dollars each to enjoy it in what they called "Gold Class". There was an hour until the film, so we went for a drink in a bar we'd walked past advertising three-dollar drinks. They weren't lying and so to celebrate my last drink for a long time, I had a sparkling wine and Aaron had a beer. We headed back to the cinema and had the best time. The thirty seats were La-Z-Boy recliners laid out in pairs with a little table in between, laid out in a room that would normally house a couple of hundred. For three dollars we had a massive glass bowl containing more popcorn than four people could eat brought to the table during the film. We also had complimentary iced water brought to us and watched the thoroughly enjoyable Guy Ritchie film with our feet up. If the film wasn't so watchable it would have been very easy to fall fast asleep, as they were the comfiest chairs we'd sat in for a long time. After the film, we had a wander to Darling Harbour and explored this until it was time to pick up Adam from the station. The harbour was gorgeous and boasted great views of the cityscape, fantastic sculptures and imaginative fountains. We took lots of photos. All in all, Aaron did a fantastic job of cheering me up after the terrible run of bad luck we'd had all week. We picked up Adam and headed back to the campsite to squeeze us all plus all our luggage into the tent (Aaron slept in between Adam and I to make it a bit less weird!). It was a surprisingly okay fit.

We decided to explore the city and the main priority was the world famous Sydney Harbour. We got the train to Central to visit Paddy's Market, which is the largest market in Australia. It was absolutely massive and I picked up some amazing bargains for my souvenirs. I posted them home via boat, so they wouldn't be there until well after I got home, but I had to watch the pennies. I was very happy with my watch to replace the one I had lost. It was kids' watch, but was only ten dollars, which was around five pounds sterling at the time, and had a picture of the Cookie Monster from *Sesame Street* on the dial and him with various other characters on the strap. I smiled every time I looked at it! It even gave Aaron a way to get me to giggle when annoyed at him. If I looked even slightly sad or cross, he just had to say, 'What time is it?' and a smile would crack across my face! (Again, simple things!) We then caught the City Circular train to arrive at the Circular Quay station. We got off the train to be immediately confronted with fantastic views of Harbour Bridge with the Opera House poking out from behind a high rise. The mass photo taking began! We followed the stream of people and walked past the ferry terminals where we were happy to find that the ferry to Manly (where we planned to go the next day) left every twenty minutes after 10am and the same coming back until after 11pm. We walked all the way around to the Opera House, which looked fantastic from a distance. Up close, however, it was very reminiscent of 1960s tired-looking concrete and was really quite ugly. Sadly, the photos from a distance didn't come out very well because it was another very grey day and the clouds seemed to blend in with the building's colouring. We went for a stroll around the botanical gardens and then headed back to the centre for a drink in the incredibly cheap bar that we had found, reaching it just as it started to spit again. It had been a very enjoyable day.

We had two days of activities left and we planned to do a bike ride around Manly, which was supposed to be one of the most picturesque places in Sydney with a beautiful beach. We had vouchers that made the bike hire very cheap indeed. We also planned to go to Bondi Beach, so we decided that the weather would decide the order. When we got up it was very cloudy, so we decided the bike ride was the better option. On the ferry ride over, however, the clouds cleared to reveal the tops of the high rises and gave us much better pictures of the bridge and Opera House. By the time we reached Manly, the weather was beautiful. The bike trail started with a nasty hill and, by the time we were halfway up, we were all wondering why we were punishing ourselves. It didn't help that we'd had to start off in the hardest gears possible and I hadn't ridden a bicycle in over ten years. The hill was relatively short and finished when we reached the beginning of the National Park, however, and it turned out to be well worth the effort. The top of the park had a viewing spot, which gave the most spectacular city view I had ever seen. It was too stunning for words because it just sounds like I am exaggerating and none of the photos do it justice. My face was genuinely purple and I had been seeing black spots for a while. When I got off my bike, I was extremely dizzy and felt on the verge of fainting. I had drunk a litre of water, but felt so hot it was ridiculous. I took off my helmet and Aaron and I headed to the shop at the top to get an ice lolly. The lady panicked when she saw me and told me to help myself to the ice water in the fridge and sit down for a bit. As I suspected, because of the black spots, my sugar levels were a bit low and the sugary lolly together with the water did me the world of good. I instantly felt refreshed and went back for a second look at the amazing panoramas. I also realised that I had only restarted the nasty methotrexate medication the day before, which made me feel incredibly ill when I first started it back in April. Still, I was happy that at least I wasn't sick this time!

The ride to the beach was so much fun because it was all downhill, so required practically no pedalling. When we reached the main beach, we did as we had been advised: to lock up the bikes (they provide bike locks, which was handy) and walk the short trail to the other beach. We discovered that this was a good move because we went from an incredibly busy beach with massive surf waves to a smaller, quieter beach with a flat, much more swimmable sea. We all dived straight in and – not for the first time on our travels – I was sure you could see steam coming off us. The sea was a lovely, refreshing temperature and we all felt much better. I was also glad to rid myself of the 'helmet hair'! We lay down on the sand and I promptly fell asleep. When I woke up and looked at the time, I was horrified to see we had half an hour to get dressed, get back to the bikes and cycle back to the shop before it shut. Luckily, we made it and we could relax again.

We finished our day in Manly with some Manly fish

and chips having turned down Manly Italians and Manly kebabs! I had garlic prawns and rice because fish and chips didn't seem to agree with me while I was on methotrexate. Every time I ate something too fatty, I was sick. We ate our dinner on the sea front watching the sunset with a woman being attacked by a seagull in front of us. It seemed insistent on sitting on her head and the man she was with was encouraging it to do so and finding it very funny. Our food was delicious and exceedingly cheap. Sydney was a lot cheaper than Perth food-wise. We were also kept entertained by a busker playing the guitar who was very talented. I was impressed with his acoustic Metallica rendition. By the time we got the ferry back, it was dark, so Adam got some incredible photos of the city by night. Unfortunately, my camera was a bit ancient and didn't cope with dark conditions very well.

The next day, we were woken again at the crack of dawn, not only by the cacophonous birds, but by the extreme heat of the early morning sun. We got up and headed to Bondi on the train. As the connecting bus pulled up at the beach, we were stunned both with how small it was and how many people were there. It was a Saturday and great weather, so we knew there would be a lot of people, but it was officially the busiest beach I had ever been on. At the top of the hill leading down to the beach, the people crowding the sand and sea looked like an army of ants and the brightly coloured lifeguards looked frantic. We headed down and once again found ourselves rushing to the sea as it was ridiculously hot. The waves were huge and there was a dangerous number of surfers. Given the size of the beach and the sheer number of swimmers I thought that the surfers should either have a designated section or have a separate beach from the swimmers like they do at other Aussie beaches we had encountered. After nearly being struck in the head, I decided to bring my session to a close and left to read my book. The boys decided to find a cheap bodyboard. They returned very pleased with themselves having found some boards for fifteen bucks and so we returned to the sea. I got wiped out twice and decided I had achieved my goal of cooling down and once more escaped the hustle and bustle of the sea. I'd lost the boys anyway. I was just about to finish my latest Gerald Durrell book when they returned very happy that they had had so much fun surfing on Bondi beach. It was late afternoon, so we headed back to the campsite to get ready for an evening of fun at the Sydney summer festival.

The next day was just dedicated to packing our stuff and trying to get it down to just the backpacks as we were getting on a plane for the first time in months. Other than my medication and my handbag, I was able to do this, so I was quite proud of myself. We washed our copious amounts of dirty washing and hung them out to dry. We then headed to the mall to keep cool as it was in the high thirties and we didn't want to dirty all our stuff again at a sandy beach. We booked a campsite with late check-in in Christchurch (New Zealand) and were happy it was only a five-minute drive from the airport. We hired a car from STA travel, which gave us great rates and would make our lives a lot easier (especially because of my joints). We then settled down for our last night in Australia.

The next morning, we were very happy it wasn't scorching hot, which made it easier to walk the fifteen minutes uphill to the train station with our backpacks. It was still incredibly painful for me, which made us even happier that we had managed to hire a car in NZ. We got the train to the airport and checked in. That was it, we were finally leaving Australia. Despite being extremely eventful and rocky at times, we had an amazing time in this country. We had countless new experiences, we found out what it was like to live there, and Adam had decided he would be more than happy to live there permanently, while Aaron had decided it was too hot for him. We met some absolutely fantastic people with whom we hoped to stay in contact. I would definitely like to come back to Australia to do all the things I originally planned to do. I would like to see Uluru in the centre, the Kimberleys in the North-West and the Great Barrier Reef in the North-East. Maybe I will be able to do so at some point in the future. Until then, I am very happy with the experiences I have already gained from the wonderful land of Aus.

CHAPTER NINE

New Zealand

Christchurch: 11/01/2010

Sydney airport is pretty big, but relatively easy to navigate. We got there in plenty of time, so we had lots of it to kill. I was worried about getting through security with my needles, but he just asked to see my passport and doctor's letter and ensured the names were identical. I was relieved! It was then on to Duty Free, then the boys had a couple of beers to use up the last of our Aussie dollars while I had a bite to eat before taking my diazepam. For some reason, I was finding it quite difficult to keep a lid on my nerves. Maybe I was worried that our run of bad luck wasn't over yet.

The plane was a lot smaller than the others we'd flown in, but we could definitely tell why Air New Zealand was voted one of the best airlines in the world all the time. The service was great and the entertainment even better. All this, together with the diazepam and Aaron allowing me to crush his fingers even when he was playing on the computer games, meant that I wasn't as bothered as I could have been by the constant and violent turbulence that we had for the whole of the three-hour flight. The seatbelt signs only came off for five minutes at a time and we were advised not to use the bathroom.

We left thirty-four-degree weather in Sydney to arrive in New Zealand at 9.30pm (thirteen hours ahead of the UK) to twelve-degree temperatures and a lot of rain. We found it absolutely freezing and I was glad I'd placed layers of warm clothing in easily accessible bags. It took an age to get through customs and it was surprisingly not due to my medication. The doctor's letter, small supply and the fact that they were pens and not syringes allowed me to sail through. However, the boys got stuck for over twenty minutes because of the three-man tent we had bought to keep accommodation costs to a minimum. Due to contamination risk procedures, they had to unpack it all and wash it (to get rid of bugs and seeds), then pack it all up again. We were the last to get through, but at last we made it to the desk to pick up our rental car. The lady was lovely and they gave us some excellent free maps of the whole of New Zealand and Christchurch itself. Adam could not have been happier to discover that our car was a Ford Focus because that was his last car back home and he loved them. I was happy too because this was the car I had learnt to drive in! We had a good time in Christchurch before heading to Methven to meet up with Adam's friend from back home.

Methven: 13/01/2010

Our check-out from the Christchurch campsite was a little delayed because I got stuck in reception when I went to pick up my medication. The nice receptionist asked me why I needed injections that needed refrigeration and then interrogated me about time-frame, symptoms and treatment. It turned out that another lady that worked there had similar symptoms, but the Kiwi medical system was apparently rubbish compared with Australia. She asked me to wait five minutes for the lady to have a chat. The swelling in her fingers certainly looked the same as mine when they were affected by my psoriatic arthritis, so she wrote down all the medication I had been put on. All they had prescribed for her was the steroids that I was on for a while. She was told she would be on them for at least two years, but I was told by my doctor that, because of their nasty side effects, you shouldn't be on them for much more than six months; they are a short-term solution only. I was only on them while the methotrexate got to work, which can take up to eight weeks to be fully effective, and then in short bursts during flare ups, yet she was offered nothing else. It really did make me count my lucky stars that I was fortunate enough to be diagnosed in Australia.

Adam's friend Johnny, nicknamed Gren, had travelled Australia and New Zealand for two years. He had found a farm job and was asked to look after his friend's hostel while he was away getting married, so he'd been in Methven (about an hour south-west of Christchurch) for about three weeks having previously lived and worked there in the ski season for seven weeks. Adam wanted to do the driving, so I sat in the back and thoroughly enjoyed the rolling landscape. It didn't look real when I looked across the incredibly flat terrain to see huge mountain ranges towering in the background; it looked like a backdrop in a film studio. This was particularly true in the drizzly, cloudy and misty weather we were experiencing. It was a shock to the system to have to wear jeans and a hoody again and still feel cold. We stopped at the occasional lookout to take pictures. When we arrived in Methven, we found the hostel and then explored the town as Johnny was still at work. It was tiny and had a population of only about 1400 people. However, it was a ski resort in the winter when the population rose to nearly 5000. This meant that there were plenty of pubs, a couple of cafés, two supermarkets, but not much else.

Johnny was very friendly. We sat and chatted in the hostel owner's living room while the boys took it in turns playing against each other on FIFA on the Xbox. Then the booze run took place. They got mixers for their whiskey (sacrilege according to Aaron) and a crate of beer. We all had a good laugh and the boys got very merry, making me jealous as I could no longer drink alcohol. We then went to get some fish and chips, which were gorgeous, but it didn't take long before I was throwing this up, as I had done every time I'd eaten them since being on the medication. This was extremely frustrating because I loved fish and chips, but calmed down after my travels as I had grown more used to the medication, and I realised it settled better if I didn't eat the batter!

Once I'd got most of it out of my system, we headed to the pub inventively named "The Blue Bar" (guess what colour it is), which was opposite the "Brown Pub"! It was a nice pub, but absolutely empty. Aaron and I had the longest game of pool ever because he was heavily intoxicated and I was heavily rubbish. It ended up with him scraping a win after about an hour.

The next morning, Aaron and I woke up at 10am after a fantastic night's sleep in a double bed. Johnny was up and about, but Adam hadn't yet emerged. Aaron and I took the car to the shops (avoiding the torrential rain) to buy stuff for a fry-up as the boys were all feeling a bit tender. We took the cat (called "Dog") to help us raise Adam from his slumber, which he did very well. Adam then cooked us a fab brunch and the fact that we were supposed to leave at 11am went speeding out of the window. We were able to fit in Johnny's bags and tent in the boot, so he decided to travel the South Island with us. So, we were soon on our way to Dunedin with me driving at 1.50pm, a little later than scheduled.

Dunedin: 14/01/2010

The drive was lovely and the car was so different to rickety old Sunny. It was a little bit boring driving an automatic, but it did mean that I only had one ankle aching because I could rest my clutch foot. I got very excited when we drove past several alpaca farms. We passed mountain after mountain laden with sheep, and there were more cows than I expected, and I was excited to see a spectacular eagle. It was a charcoal colour with a white head that looked very much like the famous American bald eagle. It was beautiful.

It was a five-hour drive to Dunedin and we arrived early evening. The campsite was stunning, but we set off as soon as we put the tents up (Adam and Johnny in one, Aaron and I in ours) to go and see the march of the penguins. This took place every evening at dusk and the receptionist told us that it happened at around 9.20pm at that time of year and it was to take about an hour to get to Sandfly Beach where you could see them from a hideout for free.

So, we set off up the side of a giant hill. It had its hairy moments when we were seemingly hanging over the edge of an enormous precipice. We had left early, so arrived at about 8.30pm, parked up on the top of a cliff and began the descent down the paths and sand dunes to reach the beach. The thought crossed my mind that I would get stuck at the bottom because the slope was unbelievably steep and long, so I worried that I might not be able to get back up. The beach was gorgeous. It was dotted with the biggest seaweed I have ever seen, some of which had strange pods that looked remarkably like pickled onions. We crossed the beach to reach the far end where the hideout was. The sun was fairly low in the sky and hiding behind the cliffs, turning the sky a beautiful salmon pink colour. The waves were crashing in and up against the surrounding cliffs. When we were halfway across the beach, a lady in a fluorescent jacket approached us. She was a local volunteer and gave us some bad news. We had missed the main march, but should still give it a shot because apparently one had just landed on the rocks. Also, there were three sea lions in our path and we were told to give them a wide berth because they were (and I quote) "a little frisky"! There were two bulls fighting over a female and, as we got closer, we could see just how colossal they were. The older, larger one must have weighed well over a tonne and was bigger than Aaron. He was standing his ground and fighting off the younger one who eventually skulked off in defeat. After a few cautiously distant photos, we beat a hasty retreat to try and catch the last penguin making its way up to its burrow for the night in the sand dunes. These penguins are small and called "yellow-eyed penguins". They are a little larger than the little blue penguins found in Australia, but apparently they are the rarest penguins in the world. The sea lions are also apparently the rarest of their species in the world because they were nearly hunted to extinction two hundred years ago and have only just returned to the area to breed again. So, I was quite content if we only saw the sea lions that day.

When we reached the hideout, we found a spot that overlooked the rocks to start our hunt for the lone penguin. We saw several more sea lions frolicking on the rocks and one fast asleep on the beach, occasionally rolling over and stretching. After about half an hour, we were close to giving up on the seemingly impossible task of finding the tiny penguin needle in the massive rocky haystack. Adam and Johnny had joined us and showed us long distance photos of a penguin that had turned up and sneaked across the beach behind them. I was very jealous and thought, 'That's it, we missed the last penguin, so we may as well go.' At that moment, Aaron, in a hushed whisper, exclaimed, 'There's one!' He pointed to the side of the grassy cliff to where a tiny penguin was scurrying and hopping up the rocky part at the bottom. The zoom on my camera was terrible, but Aaron got some pretty good photos of it. We continued to watch its painfully slow progress up the slope until we eventually lost sight of it over the brow of the hill. That was it, the last yellow-eyed penguin to reach its burrow that evening.

Having taken us ten minutes to get down to the beach (well, a matter of seconds for the boys who ran and frolicked like excited children), it took us a painful forty minutes to get back up to the car. We went to find something to eat in the very pretty city centre. It was then back to the campsite where I went to bed early after a very tiring, but thoroughly enjoyable day.

Queenstown: 15/01/2010

Jonny had been to Queenstown before and so really wanted to take us to a place called Ferg Burger, which apparently had the best burgers in the world and is a rite of passage for everyone who goes there. In fact, since leaving, anyone that hears we've been to Queenstown having been there themselves asks if we went there! Adam had the "Mr Big", which had two burgers, cheese, bacon and a whole lot of other stuff. It was a good job he was incredibly hungry. I had the "Ferg with blue cheese" and it was absolutely beautiful. Aaron had the "Bambi", which was a venison burger with plum chutney. He loved it so much that he went back for another one the next day and didn't even complain about having to queue for forty minutes in the heat!

We had a great time in Queenstown sightseeing, eating fab food and partying, and it was definitely my favourite place in New Zealand and ranks very highly in my favourite places in the world. The atmosphere is just fantastic with a buzzing nightlife and, as for the scenery – words simply do no justice to it so I won't even try.

Fox Glacier and Greymouth: 17/01/2010

We got up early in the morning because we had a big day ahead of us. I wasn't thrilled with the Queenstown campsite because there weren't freezers to freeze my ice blocks to keep my medication cool, the showers cost a dollar for just eight minutes and it was just too big. We set off on the drive to Fox Glacier and it was my turn to drive. It was interesting and a bit disturbing to see the posts marking where the glacier used to reach because it is receding at an alarming rate. It was an hour round trip to walk to the glacier and back, and it was pretty precarious because the river changes its path so frequently that they can't lay proper paths. They did have workers there moving large rocks to aid people in crossing the streams, which I thought was really good. From the bottom, the views of the cliff sides gouged by the glacier were spectacular and there were beautiful waterfalls flowing down them. The glacier itself had to be viewed from a bit of a distance because it was dangerously unstable. It was a great view, though. It was a strange blue colour and was a block with an arched tunnel at the bottom of the centre with a river surging out of it. It was the first glacier I'd ever seen and I was lost for words. It was a great new experience to add to the list.

We made the walk back to the car and I was relieved that there were no breaks or sprains for any of us. I had found the walking really challenging, though. It was then off on the short two-hour drive to Greymouth. Our pitch at the new campsite was right next to the path to the seashore, so within seconds we could be on a gorgeous pebble beach, which is where I watched the sunset. It was also where the boys had a big bonfire after dinner, as did a few other small groups of people. There was tonnes of dry driftwood, so it kept them entertained for hours, allowing me to get some peace and quiet and a nice early night. I got a few sore toes on my way back to the tent by kicking something spiky. When I shone my torch on it, it instantly balled up – I hope I didn't give the poor hedgehog a headache!

Hanmer Springs and Kaikoura: 19/01/2010

We checked out of the campsite and Adam drove us to Hanmer Springs. This was another mountainous drive and he got pretty frustrated by the U-turns. I was glad I could enjoy the view properly, but found it hard to stay awake as I always do when I'm a passenger. There is something about the vibrations and motion of a moving vehicle that makes my eyelids droop. Fatigue is also a huge part of autoimmune diseases, which didn't help! It was very strange when we got further up the mountains and could see how low the clouds were. They covered the mountaintops and it looked unreal. There were also some weird and wonderful smells when we got up that high. There was the lovely, fresh alpine smell for which so many air fresheners strive without achieving. There was also the not-so-fresh smell of the farm animals; we passed lots of sheep and a few goat farms.

After a few hours, we made it to Hanmer. This is where naturally hot springs erupt from the earth, so a big spa resort had been built over the top of it. Luckily for us, it was very reasonably priced, so we got our swimming stuff and went in. It was an amazing place with the springs ranging from thirty-three to forty-one degrees. Even the water flumes and swimming pools were fairly warm considering the weather had turned cold and miserable again. The forty-one-degree pool was a bit too warm for my liking, as it made me feel like I was cooking. I was happy when the boys wanted to change to a cooler pool because I had turned a worrying shade of pink and felt a little dizzy! My favourite pool was the thirty-five-degree one because it was like a soothing bath that didn't get cold. Despite my reservations about the corporates taking over natural beauty spots, I appreciated the fact that without a company manufacturing fake rocks that were smooth and comfortable to sit and lie on, we would be acquiring cuts and bruises from naturally uncomfortable materials. We would also most likely be surrounded by naturally occurring (and otherwise) waste with no one feeling obliged to clean it up. Warmth and particularly warm water soothes my aches and pains to this day.

After setting up the tent for what felt like the hundredth time, we got back in the car and headed to one of the beaches that was home to a seal sanctuary. I didn't get my hopes up after the lone yellow-eyed penguin fiasco because I didn't want to be disappointed. We pulled up in the little car park, which was right on the rocky beach and piled out in our winter woollies because it had turned so much colder. We looked over the ledge down to the beach a foot below and what should we see two feet away? It was a large seal fast asleep, upside-down on a rock. We could see all of its little whiskers and it had a very puppy-like face. That was it, I was in love. A little way away, we saw a few more seals sleeping on rocks and some splashing around in rock pools. They were absolutely gorgeous and we got some great photos. We even went so far as to get our feet wet in the freezing cold rock pools. They were mostly asleep or very sleepy because they hunt at sea for as long as three weeks, so need lots of rest when they finally come ashore. They felt like kindred spirits! I was very happy.

That night was our last night with Gren, so we had a bite to eat and then headed to the pub for a quick drink.

The pub we found had a beer on called "Sheep Shaggers", which kept us highly amused for an embarrassingly childishly long time. Aaron and I thrashed them at pool on a very small table, which had the biggest balls I have ever seen (certainly no clean jokes about that). We then headed back to the campsite where the boys had a crate of beer and a cask of wine to keep them happy. This was the first campsite where the games room was open twenty-four hours, so we had a surprisingly fun night playing ping pong, air hockey and playing on Adam's laptop. We finally headed to bed at about 3am and I was very happy to see my pillow; it seemed much harder to stay awake into the wee hours without alcohol, but that may have also been a combination of my arthritis and medication.

The next morning, we went to find a cheap full English breakfast to try and make the boys' recovery a little easier. We found this in a really nice pub. It was then time for a pretty difficult goodbye to Gren as he got on the bus back to Methven because we'd had such a great time with him over the last few days. We said goodbye to Kaikoura and we were on our way to Nelson on the North coast.

Nelson and Picton: 20/01/2010

It was fabulous weather when we arrived in Nelson. It was certainly living up to its reputation as being the sunniest town in the South Island and it made a lovely change to the miserable weather we'd experienced everywhere except

Queenstown. The beach and the city centre were lovely to explore.

The morning of our departure, we woke to the hardest rain and gale force winds that we had seen yet and it showed no signs of letting up. We didn't want to get all of our clean clothes wet by packing in the wet, so we shoved everything in the boot of the car and put the tent, unpacked, on the floor of the rear passenger seat as it was drenched (as were we – my waterproof mac didn't hold up to the beating that the rain was giving us). We then set off for Picton with plenty of time to get there, get packed up somewhere dry, drop the car off, get the ferry to Wellington on the North island and pick up our new car there. Or so we thought. The combination of torrential rain and roadworks made for unbelievably slow progress. We couldn't find any cover in Picton to pack up in the dry, so we parked at a supermarket and went in to get lunch for later. When we emerged, we found there was finally a break in the rain, so we scurried about packing the tent and our bags and rushed to the ferry terminal. When we arrived, though, Adam discovered he'd left a bag with his laptop in the car park in our rush and had to go back for it. By the time he got back and we handed the car keys over, we had minutes to get to the ferry and we got to the check-in desk just as it was closing. My heart skipped a beat, but we were very lucky because they allowed us on, especially because our tickets were non-refundable. They reopened the desk and raised the barrier. I was very grateful to say the least, but it was so embarrassing to walk onto the ferry with everyone giving us dark looks for holding them up.

Despite the weather, the crossing was very pleasant and we settled down in the bar for the three-hour journey. In no time at all, we were beginning the second half of our New Zealand tour.

Wellington: 21/01/2010

Adam ventured out on his own to go and meet up with a friend from back home. Aaron and I headed out a little while later. I wanted to go to the national museum of New Zealand called "Te Papa" because they had the only colossal squid on display in the whole world. We looked a little ridiculous because we were wearing shorts, flip-flops and cagoules with the hoods up and tightened, but soggy jeans, socks and trainers are thoroughly unpleasant. As my mum always said, legs dry quicker than clothes, plus it wasn't too cold. We got the train to the city and I didn't notice any stops on the whole journey. I had my head rested on Aaron's shoulder and he had his head rested on mine. The next thing either of us knew was an old couple waking us up and saying, 'You don't want to go all the way back, now, do you?' Indeed we didn't, so we thanked them very much and felt incredibly embarrassed that we'd succumbed to the warmth and comfort, whilst asking ourselves if either of us was snoring. Did we have our mouths open? We must have looked like a right pair!

By the time we got to the museum, it was only open another hour, so we headed straight to the exhibition of natural history. There was a great exhibit showing exactly how New Zealand was formed by volcanoes and how it will continue to change. You could even experience an earthquake in a little shaking house. Then we found the squid. Only eight colossal squids had been found in the whole world and only two had been whole. This was one of them, except it did have an eye missing and some skin peeling. It was over four metres long and suspended in liquid. It was very impressive and I would certainly never like to meet one swimming. Its gigantic tentacles had terrifying barbs as well as the suckers, which draw its prey up to its parrot-like beak. What we found quite amusing, though, was that it has to eat in ridiculously small chunks because its food pipe is very narrow and goes straight through the middle of the brain: anything bigger than a golf ball could result in brain damage. This must be highly frustrating for a creature so big!

Rotorua: 23/01/2010

Low and behold, it was still raining on the morning of our check-out to head up to Rotorua. The camp kitchen was on top of a hill, but had a fairly substantial porch. We took advantage of this by carrying the tent up there to take it down in relative the dry in order to stop the inner layer getting too soggy. This worked pretty well except that I kept getting told off for being distracted by the giant stick insect on the kitchen doorstep. It was huge, about eight inches, and I loved the way it raised its two front legs and swayed from side to side; it looked like it was dancing. I read on Wikipedia that they are thought to do this either to look like vegetation swaying in the breeze or as a mechanism to "discriminate objects from the background by their relative movement, a visual mechanism typical of simpler animals".

It was then off to Rotorua, once more feeling rather damp. By the time we got to the campsite there was a break in the rain, so we could go into the office to book a tent pitch. To our horror, there was a reggae festival in town, so they were all booked up. She said most places would be, which made us pretty worried. She made a few phone calls on our behalf and finally got us in on the last pitch in a campsite twenty minutes away. As luck would have it, this was right on the lake and a lot more beautiful than where we'd originally planned to stay. My mum's phrase again sprang to mind: everything happens for a reason. We had to wait for another brief pause in the rain to get our tent up and it looked pretty unstable perched on top of the hill, but at last we had somewhere dry to sleep for the one night we had there.

Our reason for visiting Rotorua was the geysers for which it is famous. But that evening I was to fulfil one of my objectives for New Zealand, which was to see a kiwi. After dark at about 9pm, we headed to the kiwi sanctuary to see the strange nocturnal birds in their native habitat. The sanctuary stays open until 11pm so that this is possible, and I was very excited. The first thing we saw when we entered the sanctuary was the massive pool housing the biggest trout I had seen in my whole life. They were bigger than the biggest salmon I had seen. They were free to come and go as they pleased because the pool was fed by a stream, which lead to Rotorua Lake. We saw some strange birds called keas, which are brown forest parrots and supposed to be some of the most intelligent birds on the planet. One of them, called Jenny, had to be kept on her own. She was hand-reared and when they tried to introduce a mate, she'd killed him! She liked to speak, but not when you stood there trying to get her to talk. Instead, she waited until you left and then cried the most bloodcurdling cries. We witnessed this firsthand. We also saw a little owl called a morepork; a name that I love (as would most Terry Pratchett fans).

I was a bit sad that we couldn't get to go to the hatchery, which was closed after 4pm, because I would have loved to have seen baby kiwis. I was satisfied, however, with the adult walkthrough enclosures. There were four sections for the four adults, and we had to be absolutely silent, or they'd run away. We were lucky enough to see all four of them for pretty lengthy periods of time and a couple of them were only inches away from us. Amusingly, one of them took a liking to the bottom of a girl who had lost interest and was sitting on the low wall of the enclosure, which meant we could get a brilliant up close and personal view of it whilst trying not to look as pervy as the bird! Sadly, it is this funny curiosity that has contributed to it becoming endangered. We couldn't take any pictures –they are nocturnal, so we weren't allowed to use flashes. None of our flashless photos came out, despite Aaron's valiant efforts with his fancy camera. They are such strange-looking things. They're flightless birds and, as a result, their wings have become very small through evolution. It looks like they have no wings at all. Their long, curved beaks are shoved so deep into the soil looking for grubs and insects to eat that I worried they might get stuck. They're pretty skittish creatures and dash about the place rather clumsily with the odd lumbering leap thrown in for good measure. They are truly fascinating and I can see why there is such a great effort to help them survive. To aid in the effort, I bought a cuddly kiwi for my baby brother, but I would love to do more.

We spent so long with the kiwis that we ended up not getting home until well after 11.30pm, so we pretty much went straight to bed. In the morning we were very grateful to discover it had finally stopped raining and the sun was poking its warm little face out. We had been told that the biggest and most exciting geysers were at the Maori exhibition called "Te Puia". However, when we got there, we found that it was expensive to get in at over forty dollars. All we'd wanted to do was see the geysers, so it was not a justifiable expense for us personally. We went to the information centre where I explained that we needed something we could afford and were very surprised when she told us there were some free geysers to see and marked them on our maps. When we arrived, it looked just like an English park with large expanses of grass, a playground and clusters of trees. When we looked closer, the clusters of trees had fences around them and steam rising from them: we had found some geysers. Sadly, they weren't readily erupting like the expensive ones, but they were very interesting nonetheless. A couple of them were just seemingly bottomless holes with buckets of steam rising. Some were piles of stones and rocks with steam coming off them. A couple of them were ponds (one rather large) with large clusters of bubbles rising to make it look as though the water was boiling. The most interesting for me were the muddy holes. One was really quite large, and the mud was noisily bubbling ferociously, looking as though it could erupt at any moment. There was a great heat radiating from the whole area, but what was most overwhelming was the smell. It was an intense sulphurous rotten egg smell that was difficult to get used to! A Rotoruan called Kirsty whom we met on our Australian wine tasting tour said that you never get used to it, no matter how long you live there.

Waitomo: 24/01/2010

After seeing the geysers, it was time to set off on the relatively short drive to Waitomo. This was a tiny town with only one street and it didn't even have a supermarket. The reason for coming here was the glow worm caves. We opted for a tour, which was actually very good value for money. We started at the top of the caves and our guide was a little old Maori lady. She told us that the caves were discovered by two men together. One was an English explorer and the other was a Maori elder. They entered the caves by the river at the bottom and scrambled to the top. Because he owned the land above them, the caves then belonged to the Maori and he organised tours. It turned out that he was our guide's great-grandfather, so she had a great connection and lots of stories to tell. We descended into a cave full of stalactites and stalagmites, some of which formed great shapes. My favourite chamber of the caves was called "the Cathedral". It had great stalactite organ pipes and a cavernous arched ceiling. The acoustics meant that several famous Kiwi opera singers had given concerts there. Seven people had married there, the first of whom was our guide's daughter and another was her son. When asked how you can get married there, she replied that it helps if you are marrying into the family! They also have Christmas carols every year. It was a gorgeous venue made even better when she turned out the lights and told us to look up while singing *Twinkle Twinkle Little Star*. At the highest point was a cluster of the first glow worms I had ever seen. They were beautiful and looked very much like twinkly stars.

We then descended to the river where there was a boat waiting for us. There was only room for half the trip plus the guide, so the families and the elderly went first and the rest of us waited for the guide to come back and pick us up. As the boat left us, the only sound we could hear was a ringing as the eerie silence seemed to press in on our ears. As we looked around, we couldn't help but feel as though we were in the opening scenes of a horror film; abandoned with something terrible about to happen! A fantastic view opened up in front of us as our eyes got used to the dark with glow worms covering the cave ceiling. The overhangs allowed us to get very close and you could see the tiny glowing grubs with their sticky silk threads hanging down to catch their prey like spider webs. They were weirdly beautiful.

Finally the boat returned with our guide and we clambered aboard. Our guide pulled us through the caves using ropes attached to the ceiling. It is impossible to describe the views of the thousands of glow worms in the pitch dark. There were so many that they cast an impressive light down on us and we were stunned into silence. It was truly spectacular. We left the caves via the lower entrance from where they had first been discovered. We made the climb back to the car and headed back to camp for the evening. We set off to Caramundel the next day, a stop on the way to Auckland.

Auckland: 26/01/2010

We pitched our tent in a campsite near the airport, which was in a suburb called Manakau. We just chose to relax the afternoon we arrived and get all our washing done because we knew it would be a busy day for Aaron's birthday the following day. The next morning, we had a lie-in on request of the birthday boy. We then went to an all-you-can-eat buffet restaurant for lunch. The food was lovely. The highlight was the smoked joint of roast ham, which was to die for. The extensive selection of desserts was also highly enjoyable. We all ate so much that a 'wafer thin mint' would have had similar consequences to the large chap in the Monty Python film *The Meaning of Life*!

Way back in Hong Kong at the beginning of our trip, we met two guys on a crazy night out called Chris and Craig. They went from there straight to New Zealand and said we should meet up. Adam and I chatted to them on Facebook during the day and arranged to meet them after they finished work. Chris was managing a restaurant and finished at 10.30pm, so we went to a bar called the Queen's Ferry Hotel just off Queen Street, which he recommended, before meeting him in a bar opposite his work called Mybar. The Queen's Ferry was a very nice little pub and said it was the oldest pub in Auckland. It was very quaint, but pretty expensive. When we got to Mybar, we couldn't see him anywhere, so we asked the barman if he'd seen him. The girl sitting at the bar said she was his girlfriend, and he was running late. It wasn't long until Chris turned up and very soon the drinks and the catch-up conversations were flowing. He was as lovely as we remembered from the incredibly drunken Hong Kong night with him and we had a blast. When it got to about midnight we all headed off to meet Craig in the bar he was managing. Craig's bar was empty, so he put on a show for us by doing fancy shooters. He put a couple of straws on top of each tumbler and balanced a shot of Jägermeister on top of those. He told us to stand well back, put some alcohol in his mouth, then created an impressive flamethrower with a lighter and lit all the shots. It was very entertaining. He plied the boys with free drinks, and I had fruit juice. Needless to say, Aaron had a fantastic night as we all did and he doesn't remember getting home, which was always a sign of a good birthday!

It was very difficult getting up in time to check out at 10am the next morning, but somehow we managed it. We headed to the airport feeling a little sad that we were leaving New Zealand as we'd all had such an amazing time. Despite the rain, it was definitely a highlight of the trip. When I come back it will be with plenty of money and time to do all the activities we couldn't do at the time.

CHAPTER TEN

Island Life

Fiji

We could feel the temperature rising as we got closer to Fiji and we were getting very excited. As we flew closer, I could see it very clearly. There was the lush green island, beautiful sandy beaches and a strange ring in the sea with waves breaking against it. This was because the beach plateaued under the water for a few hundred metres and then dropped about a mile to deep sea. It looked bizarre. At the exit to the airport, a little band was playing cheery, laid-back music on guitars and singing. Some Fijian ladies working in the airport tried to find our hotel transfer, but it had taken so long to get through customs that it had left without us, so we had to get a taxi. It ended up working out ten Fijian dollars cheaper than the transfer would have been for the three of us and our driver was lovely. We went through the main town of Nadi, which didn't look much different to the villages except that it had a garage and a couple of shops: it was tiny. The scenery was very much like the rural areas of Thailand with small shanty-looking villages dotted along the dusty, pot-holed road. A lot of the buildings we saw in the villages were built on stilts, but I couldn't find out exactly why this was. Perhaps it was to keep animals out, or due to a risk of flooding. I read that in Samoa, the higher the elevation of the house, the more important the inhabitants, so maybe it was the same in Fiji. We had to stop at one stage because a cow was crossing the road dragging its tether with a clod of earth behind it with its owner standing with his hands on his head looking exasperated! The taxi driver thought that this was hilarious. We even saw a huge game of football with sticks being used as makeshift goal posts. They seemed to be having a fantastic time.

When we finally arrived at our destination, it looked more like a resort than a hostel and I began to worry that the price on the website was wrong. Luckily it wasn't. We were shown to our room by the security guard who was nice enough to carry my bag for me because I was struggling. He opened the door and led us up a wooden staircase, which opened up to a massive room with four separate single beds and we had the whole room to ourselves. It was gorgeous. They kindly kept the restaurant open for us so that we could have a late dinner. We had a pleasant meal with a great three-piece guitar band singing for us and chatted to a Brazilian guy on the table next to us. We were exhausted, so we soon headed up for an early night. The Fijian hospitality was by far the best on the whole trip. They were all so welcoming, laid-back and friendly. It's hard to believe that it wasn't much more than a hundred years ago that they may have eaten us! We were looking forward to a relaxing four days there. There wasn't much to do, so it was lovely to be able to do nothing without feeling guilty or disappointed that we were missing out on something.

It didn't disappoint. We spent our time in the pool, snorkelling on the nearby reefs, eating amazing food and learning about the local culture. I went on the hunt for mudskippers (they were fascinating!) and spent hours watching fiddler crabs. We had had such a fabulous time that we were sad to leave Fiji after only a few days. But, we still had the Cook Islands to look forward to, fantastic memories and lovely new people we'd met.

The Cook Islands: 02/02/2010

It was very strange that we left Fiji at 11.30am on the 2nd of February and arrived in the Cook Islands at 2.30am on the 2nd of February. We had lost a whole day to travelling, but had the chance to repeat it like going back in time! It made me wonder just how fast our plane was flying and when we got off I half expected to see either Superman holding the plane or flaming tyre marks behind it with a crazy professor celebrating! We headed outside and found Bill who was meeting us with our free transfer to the hostel on the west coast of Rarotonga (the main island). The hostel seemed pretty basic, but we were so tired that we just hit the sack as soon as we arrived.

That night, the owner of the hostel, a Maori woman called Tisa, invited us to take part in a traditional Cook Islands buffet. It took her and her family all day to prepare and for only four pounds each we could eat as much as we liked. They have the same potato-like substance that the Fijians call cassava, but they called it something else. With this, they made potato salad, thick-cut crisps, spicy patties and steamed dumplings (very similar to German kartoffelkloesser, but flavoured with pineapple). There was an absolutely gorgeous crab salad, ceviche to die for (raw fish marinated with lime and other ingredients to effectively cook it – Cook Islanders call it 'ika') and various other delights. There was nothing that I didn't like, but it was all quite stodgy, and I was completely over-full after only a little bit of everything. We made friends with the backpackers at our table while there was a group of guys playing very loud drinking games. When they were done, a couple came and sat with us too; Mick was Dutch and Julian was German. Everyone was really nice and we chatted well into the night.

The next day, we headed to the nearby cafe for the boys to have the biggest full English breakfast they'd had all trip and I had a whopping great pile of delicious pancakes. They were the size of side plates and fantastically light and fluffy, but there were five of them plus maple syrup, so Adam had to help me finish! We headed to the beach to hang out with hostel people and I was happy to see that a few minutes' walk down the beach gave us a larger rock-free patch of sea to make it possible to swim. We did have to stay off our feet as much as possible, though, to try and avoid stepping on the hundreds of sea cucumbers – an animal I'd had a slight obsession with as a child – littering the sea floor. The locals call them "rori" and actually eat them. The boys were happier playing with them like a cross between a ball and a bean bag. They are weirdly squishy if you step on them and if they beach themselves they spill their guts everywhere, which is supposedly as a defence mechanism, but clearly doesn't work in this circumstance and looks horrendous. We had a lot of fun playing frisbee and chatting, plus I had a lot of fun playing with hermit crabs.

Our days were spent relaxing on the beach, and our evenings were spent partying with the new friends we'd made at our hostel, including a great night out. It was odd for me experiencing "party island" totally sober, but I still had a great time, as did the boys.

CHAPTER ELEVEN

USA

Los Angeles

J ulian, the German guy we met in the Cook Islands, joined us for the final leg of our trip. We had two full days in LA and then saved on accommodation costs for a night by booking an overnight bus ride to San Francisco. We booked a minibus tour to see as much of LA as we could in the short time we were there. We saw celebrity homes in Beverly Hills, Sunset Boulevard, Rodeo Drive and all the sights, and we had a great time with the guide.

That evening, we headed down Vine Street, which crosses Hollywood Boulevard and is part of the walk of fame. It was the grand unveiling of Ringo Starr's star to mark the walk of fame's fiftieth anniversary. We got there just in time for his speech and could see him pretty clearly. It was quite hard to hear him, but we still heard him say "peace and love" several times. When they finally unveiled his star, which was outside the famous Capital Records building (which looks like a stack of records), an explosion of ticker tape came over the crowd.

Everyone kept telling us the next day that the weather was very unusual, but to us the fact that it poured down with rain on our last day in LA was just typical of our trip, so we spent time in the Grammy Museum. We had dinner at In-n-Out Burger, which we were told by American Aaron in the Cook Islands was the best burger chain in America. He was right, it was lovely!

San Francisco: 10/02/2010

The Greyhound bus was the total opposite of the relative luxury its Australian counterpart provided. When we got on, there was an overwhelming smell of sweaty feet, body odour and marijuana. Although we got used to the smell, the man opposite with the most erratic and ear-piercing snore I have ever heard prevented any of us from getting more than an hour of sleep the whole way. We arrived at our hostel at 6am, but luckily our room was available, so we went straight to bed to get some much-needed sleep. We felt bad that the two people already sleeping in the dorm we were to inhabit got disturbed as we attempted to make our beds quietly, but we really needed to get our heads down as soon as possible.

We had an amazing time exploring this incredible city, and I would very happily revisit. We had fun playing cards in the evenings because Julian taught us a great German card game called 'Schwimmen'. This brought our card game knowledge up to four games! We were there for Valentine's Day, and Aaron and I enjoyed a lovely meal together on Fisherman's Wharf.

We were sad to leave San Francisco because it was an absolutely fantastic city, but we were looking forward to our next stop.

Viva Las Vegas: 16/02/2010

We had a gruelling fifteen-hour bus ride ahead of us because we had to transfer at LA. This was very frustrating because we were going back on ourselves, but we hadn't been able to book an internal flight as planned because it was a holiday weekend. Luckily there wasn't a snorer on this bus, so from about 11.30pm until dawn we all managed to sleep. Aaron and I then got a bit more on the second bus, so we felt pretty good, plus it made the journey pass very quickly.

We arrived in Las Vegas at 2.30pm and it was very exciting to see all the billboards advertising the fabulously tacky shows. We could see our hotel from anywhere in Downtown Las Vegas because the Stratosphere's tower had the highest observation deck in the US and was the tallest building in Las Vegas (it was used in the film *Domino* with Keira Knightley). As we walked through the front doors we were hit by a wall of flashing lights and noises. It was so kitsch and I loved it! We checked in and headed to our massive room. We were paying less than we were for the hostels in San Francisco and yet we didn't have to sleep in bunk beds; we had two luxuriously comfortable double beds, great views of the city, an en suite with bath and shower, plus our own TV. Heavenly! We all took much-needed showers before heading downstairs to the casino. The boys got all-you-can-drink wristbands from the bar and we played on the machines. I lost eight dollars, Adam lost a tiny bit, Aaron was up a little and Julian was up enough to cover his drinks, dinner and still have a profit!

Residents of the hotel got free access to the tower (which normally costs quite a lot). We had to go through airport-style security to get to the lift. I suddenly panicked when the lift slowed down its near light-speed velocity near to the top. We had to wait for the pressure to equalise before the doors could open, which was very scary. It was the highest I'd ever been without being in an aeroplane and my heart was racing as Aaron led me out onto the enclosed observation deck with a fabulous view opening up in front of us. All the lights of Vegas were shining, but it took a while for me to calm down and control the tears. I just couldn't get the thought of being 108 floors up and fearing for my life out of my head. But, Aaron kept hold of my hand and we were able to make it all the way around the observation deck. It did make me feel unsafe that all the windows had signs saying "Please don't lean on the glass", though. We decided to save the outdoor observation deck and the thrill rides on the floor above for another night; perhaps a night with diazepam! We were very tired and retired to bed.

The next day, Aaron and I were confined to the room

with the lurgy. We were thoroughly miserable that we had caught stomach bugs on our last few days of our world trip, but it was typical of our whole year. We couldn't risk being more than twenty feet from the bathroom, so we were cooped up for two days. I was grateful that we had such a lovely hotel room and great films to watch. We were also grateful to have Julian with us because it meant that Adam wasn't left on his own and those two had an absolute blast. We were gutted to have missed out on a lot. We had wanted to go on a day trip to the Grand Canyon and see a show, but couldn't do either of those. At least this, coupled with the lack of gambling and no food, saved us a small fortune.

Julian's last day in Vegas was the day before ours because he had to get back to LA for his flight. Aaron and I started to feel a bit better by early evening, so we could leave the sanctuary of the en-suite room to celebrate with him (minus the alcohol). We caught the water and fire show at The Mirage, which truly was spectacular. It was like volcanoes erupting. We then walked down to the Bellagio next to Caesar's Palace to see the dancing waters. This was quite a trek, especially because Aaron and I were exhausted having had no energy to begin with. The Caesar's Palace complex was immense, and I was looking forward to seeing inside. We knew of the Bellagio from the film *The Hangover*. The building itself was impressive, but the dancing waters, which are perfectly choreographed to music, are indescribable. It was an amazing experience. Aaron and I watched two shows (they are every fifteen minutes in the evening), then headed inside to check out the casino. Adam and Julian watched more shows as they'd already seen inside while we were ill.

Very early the next morning, we said a sad goodbye to Julian and enjoyed the last day of our travels by eating, drinking and having fun gambling on our limited budgets.

We dragged ourselves out of bed the following morning to have showers and check out. It made me laugh that there was even a mini casino in the departure lounge of the airport. It was also very weird that every voice we heard had a British accent. We had not heard that many in one place for a year and it made the fact that we were flying home very real indeed. Our plane was a massive double-decker Boeing, which made me feel a bit safer because the inside looks less like a plane, and we didn't feel as many bumps.

The flight itself was fine, there was no turbulence, and the landing was so incredible that we hardly felt the wheels touch the ground. There were a couple of moments during the night that my eyes had welled up at the thought of being so close to home. Although I was sad that our adventures were ending, I was also incredibly overjoyed to be seeing my mum, my family and friends very soon. This was confirmed when I finally got to hug my mum at the airport and we both burst into tears. I was so relieved to be finally home and very happy to have such great stories to tell of our fabulous travels. Now it was time to enter the real world.

PART THREE

The Real World

CHAPTER TWELVE

The Start and End of My Dream Career

aron and I had two main goals for when we finished travelling: start our careers and save up to buy a house. To help us with the latter, my mum invited us to live with her again, instead of (as she put it) "throwing our money down the rental hole". We were very grateful to be moving back in with her, and I saw it as a great sign that the police were recruiting when we got back home. It felt like fateful timing. I gathered my courage and hit "apply". I was first invited to do an online application process, and so settled in to be quizzed. The first screen appeared with the first question:

Do you suffer from any of the following illnesses
or conditions?

The first option was any heart-related illnesses. The second was any inflammatory arthritis. I had no choice but to tick that box and continue. The next screen made my heart fall through my stomach. It said that they were very sorry, but

I could no longer apply to join the police because of my health. I was floored. I felt like, although I'd been through some tough times health-wise, it was well under control with my medication, and I was healthy, fit and active. It hadn't even occurred to me that they wouldn't even let me get past the first page of the application process. My dream career had come to a halt before it had even started, and I had no idea what I was going to do.

Added to that, another spanner was thrown into the works because I wasn't able to get an appointment with a rheumatologist quickly. I'd only had enough medication to get me home, assuming that I'd be seen quickly on my return because I had an existing diagnosis, and my Australian rheumatologist had given me all the paperwork he'd thought I'd need. It had taken five days between the referral from the GP to seeing a rheumatologist in Perth, Australia. However, it took five months for the same process in the UK, even with an existing diagnosis. The two medical systems work very differently. Australia has the advantage of a smaller population, and a healthcare system that they pay for, whilst recouping around two-thirds of that outlay with Medicare and – for a lot of people – the rest via insurance. I was just going to have to be patient.

Aaron and I were finding it tricky to get jobs thanks to the market changes from the crash whilst we were away. So we both had our first experience of the job centre and signing on while we were job hunting. It wasn't a very pleasant experience, but we were grateful for the safety net. Luckily, we only needed one payment before we both successfully secured employment. Aaron found a job within the field of chemistry, which seemed to suit him very well. In the meantime, I was applying for everything and anything because I had no idea what I wanted to do. I had a few successful interviews and was lucky enough to have a choice of what I wanted to do. One was in administration, but heading up a small company as they wanted to grow. It was really decent money. I was offered that first, but held off on accepting because the job I really wanted (even though it was lower pay) was still in the mix. My mum had found an advert in the local paper (yes, that's how long ago it was, we used to trawl the jobs section of the newspapers!) for a publishing house, looking for someone to work in the warehouse picking and packing book orders, as well as admin for the various departments. The interview went swimmingly, we were all giggling at my terrible jokes and it seemed like a great fit, so I was offered that job too, and I immediately accepted.

It was a small company, with only five people other than me. The two managing directors were a married couple, and the two members of the production team were also a couple. That left one other girl and me. She left the company shortly after I started (was it something I said?!) and so I spent most lunchtimes on my own having a walk or sitting in my car, as I felt a bit like a fifth wheel in the office! But they soon employed someone to take over the vacant role and I finally had someone to talk to. We're still great friends today!

The issues with my health made picking and packing

the book orders tricky some days, but I appreciated the opportunity to stay active, whilst having the admin to give me a break when I needed it. I was lucky to be given work from all of the departments with a view to me choosing which department I'd like to progress through. I chose the production department because I fell in love with creating books. The editing, the design, the feeling of realising authors' dreams, it all combined to make me fall in love with books in a new way.

During this time, I'd been waiting to be seen by a rheumatologist. I'd been honest from the interview stage that I had a chronic illness, and for the most part I was doing okay at managing it. However, five months off the medication were beginning to take their toll and I was starting to struggle. When I was eventually seen, although I was prescribed the same medication (which then took another month to be delivered, so I was off it for six months altogether), I didn't feel the benefits that I felt when I started it in Australia. Several months in to injecting the Humira and I didn't feel like it was doing anything at all. The rheumatologist said that unfortunately they'd been finding other patients experiencing the same thing, after a significant break from it they were finding it was less effective when restarted. I was gutted. It had been my wonder drug. It had been so successful with me that I'd stopped worrying about having a chronic illness, and hadn't thought about the long-term because I could almost pretend I didn't have it. At that moment, I started to worry that I would never feel "normal" again.

I also had an additional diagnosis of fibromyalgia (you can read more about this from Versus Arthritis here: https://www.versusarthritis.org/about-arthritis/conditions/fibromyalgia/). The worst symptoms for me were pain when I was knocked on the backs of my arms, my thighs and my chest. When I would get knocked on these main pressure points, it would feel like an explosion under my skin, building to a crescendo before fading away. It also affected my sleep, so for a while when it was really out of control I was prescribed amitriptyline, which did help. When I first start this drug it can make me feel like I have a hangover the day after for a number of days, but I soon get used to it. Unfortunately, my body seems to get used to the drug quite quickly too, and it stops working after a while.

There are a number of different options for medicating my types of arthritis. Anti-TNF is one of them. It is under the umbrella term "biological therapy" and works by suppressing a protein called "tumour necrosis factor", a part of the immune system response that can increase inflammation when excess amounts are found in the blood or joints. When it was clear the Humira was no longer working, I was put on a different type of anti-TNF called golimumab (quite the mouthful!). One of the side effects of this type of medication is that some patients find that they catch every little bug going round. I was also put back on to methotrexate (a "disease modifying anti-rheumatic drug", or DMARD), so had a double whammy of immunosuppressants.

While the golimumab and methotrexate combination

worked okay, I still had to have anti-inflammatory medication prescribed over the top to keep more in control of my arthritis. I worked in an open-plan office (when I was promoted into the production department and out of the warehouse, my little bubble of half the day to myself was removed) and I was off sick more than anyone else in the company. If someone had a cold, I was pretty much guaranteed to catch it, but with the cold I'd most often get a throat infection on top, I'd lose my voice, and would be hit harder by a seemingly "normal" bug than anyone else. It would take me longer to recover but would also cause my inflammation to increase (if the immune system is fighting something off, it usually increases the levels of white blood cells and proteins that with my disease cause my joints to swell more), so I would also be in more pain and have more fatigue.

Despite this, I was good at my job, and really passionate about it, so I progressed through the company until I was the "Group Head of Production", looking after the teams producing the books across all the imprints within the company, including a traditional imprint, a partnership publishing imprint and a huge self-publishing imprint. I absolutely loved it. I got to work directly with authors, on all genres of books, and had amazing teams to look after as the company had grown. However, my health caused a lot of issues. The job was intense and brought a lot of stress with it. Stress and chronic conditions do not mix well, and boy do I know that now! It became a vicious circle of picking up all the bugs going, stressing about being off sick knowing I'd have work to catch up on and knowing my colleagues would be having to pick up the slack in my absence, getting back to the office and working hard to catch up whilst worrying about catching another bug, feeling stressed, and then picking something else up. I felt like a bit of a mess, the stress was taking its toll, and my arthritis felt out of control.

I decided to change my priorities. I didn't want to live to work, I wanted a better work-life balance, and I wanted to start a family with Aaron after we got married in 2015. We'd been through a lot with my health, but also in our personal lives. We'd lost my father-in-law to complications from his type one diabetes, and my mum was diagnosed with cancer for the second time just before our wedding. Whilst she was positive she would beat it for the second time, it was very scary to be having to go through all of that worry all over again. Something needed to change.

CHAPTER THIRTEEN

Mindset Shift

Starting a family is a scary prospect for most people, as it is a venture into the unknown. But for me this was magnified by my arthritis. One of the recurring thoughts I had during the earlier months and years of diagnosis was whether I'd be able to have children at all. Would I be able to carry them? Would I be physically able to look after children? Given that I have a genetic disease I could pass on to children, was it selfish to have children and risk them having the same thing?

I was lucky enough to go on a two-week ankylosing spondylitis residential course at Bath hospital in 2013. The two weeks involved daily physiotherapy and hydrotherapy, alongside classes in pain management and counselling for chronic illness. All whilst meeting and living with people with the same disease. It was amazing! Everyone with this disease should have this opportunity, as I learnt so much, and made friendships for life. The daily therapy worked so well that I even grew a couple of centimetres during that fortnight, as they discovered by taking our measurements at the start and end of the course! One of the worries I voiced during our sessions was my fear that I may not be able to have children, and I wasn't sure whether I should if I could. I was happy to hear that a lot of patients successfully have children, and there was a very positive discussion about why it's not selfish to do so!

With that, Aaron and I made the decision to start planning for a baby as soon as we got married. I'd been told by various rheumatology professionals (although told to relax and go at my own pace in Bath) that I would be safest to have a baby as young as possible. They said before I was thirty, but I wasn't having that, as I wanted to build my career first, plus I did not feel anywhere near ready mentally! We got married in April 2015 and with the help of my rheumatologist I came off my anti-TNF injections and methotrexate tablets. Methotrexate can harm unborn children, and they didn't have enough data to know if the golimumab did or not at that time, so I had to come off both six months before we were allowed to start trying. I managed okay during that time, but it got pretty tricky towards the end, so I was thrilled when it was finally time to come off my contraceptive in order to start trying. Over the following couple of months, I started to really struggle with my arthritis. I had an appointment with my rheumatologist who finished by saying, 'Hurry up and get pregnant, will you?!'

I replied, 'You try getting pregnant when the joint stiffness prohibits a comfortable position and you're left in pain every time!' I was given a handy leaflet on more comfortable positions with arthritis (aimed at older people suffering from osteoarthritis, so a bit of a passion killer, but still helpful!) and sent on my way. There wasn't much else anyone could do because most medications were off limits in case of pregnancy.

Meanwhile, I was still working and struggling on with my painful joints, not able to talk about it at work because I didn't want anyone to know I wasn't on my medication because we were trying for a baby. All of a sudden, I came down with a sickness bug. I threw up at work and went home ill, staying in bed for a couple of days. I frequently had tummy bugs, a regular symptom of my autoimmune diseases since before diagnosis. I sometimes wondered whether it was because my immune system was too busy fighting my own body rather than the bugs it was supposed to fight. More recently, however, my rheumatology nurse said that there's a possibility it could be Chrohn's, another autoimmune disease. So, there may be more investigations to come in the future. When the sickness from this particular bug eased, although I was still feeling pretty unwell, I went back into work. For the next couple of weeks, I still felt really sick but managed to get by. It wasn't unusual for a sickness bug to leave me wiped out and nauseous for several weeks after. However, I seemed to feel worse if someone cooked something smelly in the microwave on our lunch break, or if I was particularly hungry. One of the girls in the office joked that maybe I was pregnant, but I was on my period, so I knew it couldn't be that.

One evening, I was settling in for a night in with Aaron and he was opening a bottle of wine. I gratefully accepted the glass, but when I gave it a sniff, my stomach turned. It smelt like cabbage, so I said, 'Urgh! This wine is off!' I gave it a taste to make sure and it was definitely well and truly off. Aaron looked at me, sniffed his own wine and claimed that it smelt and tasted fine. I couldn't understand it! He carried on and drank a couple of glasses, but there was no way I could stomach it, so I left it.

I rang my mum in my car on my lunch break the following day and explained what had been going on. She said, 'You know how I found out I was pregnant? Your dad opened up a bottle of wine the first day of our camping trip and it made me sick.' Again, I explained that I had (by this time) just finished my period, so I couldn't possibly be pregnant, and she told me that wasn't necessarily true and I should take a test. We only had the cheap tests at home, which showed one line for not pregnant, two crossed lines for pregnant. One line was clear as day, but the other was so faint neither Aaron nor me were confident that it was there at all! So off to the shops we went to buy the more expensive digital version. This very clearly said "pregnant", which should have had us overjoyed, but we just felt weird. We had so many questions. I'd had bleeding, so could that mean I'd actually lost the baby? Hormones can still show up on a pregnancy test after a loss, so could I have been pregnant but wasn't any more? I was so confused! We took a third and final test, which was the digital one that tells you how far along you are because we had no idea thanks to the periods. The highest it went was 3+ weeks, and it said that, so we were still confused. We read up on the stages of pregnancy and saw that nausea normally happened around week seven or eight, so could I really be or have been that far along?

The next step was to make an appointment with the GP. The trouble was, with having had regular periods so far, there was no way for her to date the pregnancy so she couldn't book my twelve-week scan accurately. So we booked a private scan to date the pregnancy before booking in with the midwife. I don't think I've ever been more nervous than I was waiting with Aaron for that scan. When that gel went on and the scan started I closed my eyes and prepared myself for the news that she couldn't find a heartbeat. My eyes shot open when she said she'd found the baby and that all seemed well, though! She asked us if we'd like to hear the heartbeat and that noise filled me with joy. I was pregnant, we were having a baby! She dated the pregnancy at around ten weeks, so I went back and booked in to see the midwife.

The rest of the pregnancy was mostly filled with joy. The immunosuppressant side effects of pregnancy meant my arthritis was under control even more than when I was on medication, it felt wonderful! For me, it was like having my own immunosuppressant medication tailored exactly to my body. I had some complications due to my weight (steroids along with other factors had made me gain over three stone during the years following diagnosis), but it was mostly smooth sailing. I finished the pregnancy healthier than when I started because I'd been able to exercise so much more and was actively changing my attitude towards food for the good of the baby and me.

One of the symptoms of ankylosing spondylitis is fusion of the joints in the spine. My rheumatologist told me that not everyone with AS fuses, but I am one of the unlucky ones. My sacroiliac joints (the joints in the pelvis that open up when you're giving birth) have fused, along with the lower joints of my spine. One of the benefits of fusing is the reduction in pain once the fusion is finished because there isn't a joint left to attack any more. Over the years, the pain and inflammation in my spine has been steadily moving up it (although my neck has been affected relatively recently too). This fusion meant I was strongly advised to have a c-section to give birth safely. There was some confusion with this at first because of the ridiculous system of physical paperwork in the UK meaning the obstetrician didn't have my notes for our first appointment, then didn't have my initial MRI results showing the fusion (just the notes for the second MRI declaring no change) and so was reluctant to categorically say I needed a caesarean (I was made to feel somewhat "too posh to push" for some time, as I had to fight my corner for fear of death, both mine and the baby's!), but eventually it was booked for thirty-eight weeks.

I started my maternity leave the week before my c-section, as there were quite a few things I wanted to do around the house before the birth (not least sort out space in our bedroom for the Moses basket!), as well as wanting time to rest before the birth. I got a few bits done but was so shattered that I decided to "listen to my body" and actually put my feet up. The Wednesday of that week (my section was booked for the following Monday) I was booked in to have a haircut followed by a trip to the cinema with my friend. I'd had my last midwife appointment the day before where she'd had to come back to measure my bump because my tummy had gone tight. I told her that had happened a few times throughout the day and she said it was Braxton hicks. There was no pain, it just felt like the skin on my tummy was tightening, but she said it was nothing to worry about. So, whilst my hairdresser and her colleagues were worried about me giving birth in the salon, and my friend was worried about me giving birth in the cinema, I was pretty chilled out and looking forward to getting things done over the following couple of days ahead of the birth.

That night, I woke up with a jolt. I looked at the time and it was 12.45am. I felt a bit funny but couldn't put my finger on it, so just assumed I needed a wee. I hauled myself out of bed, got as far as the foot of the bed when there was a sudden whooshing feeling and my waters broke with a spectacular explosion. With a few expletives, I rushed to the bathroom, nearly slipping on the laminate floor as the waters were coming fast, and sat on the toilet. It wasn't slowing down, so I called to my husband, who was still fast asleep. He asked me what was up and I shouted that he needed to get my hospital maternity notes because my waters had broken. He sleepily brought them to me on the toilet and I hastily called the hospital and explained the situation. They told us to get there as quickly as possible, so I whacked in a maternity pad, grabbed a plastic bag for the car seat and my hospital bag for the car and off we went. When we got there, they weren't expecting us. It turns out I'd called the wrong hospital in my sleep-deprived state, but luckily they had room for us. My waters had already soaked through the pad and were down to my feet, so I was told to strip off, get a gown on and hop on the bed, where they strapped all the monitors to me.

Here's a note to anyone going into hospital with an existing condition: KNOW YOUR NOTES! Very few hospital staff I've met actually read your notes, proven by the comment of the midwife of, 'Oh, if it progresses slowly then you'll be on track for a natural birth.' Trying not to scream, I calmly explained that wasn't possible due to my fusion. She then said, 'Well if it progresses slowly then hopefully we can hold on until the consultant gets here.' I asked when he started and was told 6.30am. Seeing as it was only 3am, I was a bit worried about being in labour that long in case it progressed too far, whilst also wondering what was wrong with the registrar if she didn't want me operated on by them!

She left the room and my contractions started to get much more frequent. They weren't very painful, but they were uncomfortable, and I was worried that they seemed to be less than five minutes apart. Aaron and I also thought it was odd that we couldn't hear the monitor in the thick of a contraction. The midwife came back in after a few contractions and said, 'Oh, baby's misbehaving, I'll be back in a minute.' She walked out of the room and walked back in with several people, and the people seemed to just keep coming. They all started looking at the monitor, asking questions about me and a junior doctor was trying to get a canular into my hand. With one unsuccessful attempt leaving me holding my hand in the air to try and stop the bleeding while she butchered the other, it took a while for her to do it successfully! That did, however, give me a chance to ask her what on earth was going on, since everyone else had left the room. She was surprised I didn't know, but while everyone had said who they were and what their jobs were, no one had said why they were there. She informed me that my baby's heart rate was drastically dropping every time I had a contraction, possibly because she had the umbilical cord wrapped around her neck, or she was distressed and squeezing it, but either way she had to come out with an emergency c-section as soon as possible.

It was a whirlwind of people doing things to me, moving me to theatre, getting the spinal done and talking me through the procedure, and within half an hour our beautiful baby Lily was born. The next few hours are a bit of blur thanks to the cocktail of drugs pumped into me, but when the registrar had finished sewing me up, he came round to my head and said, 'It looks like Lily had a guardian angel today.' I wasn't sure if he said that to all his patients, but it took me aback a little. Aaron then asked me if people usually talked about the placenta in such detail because we could hear it being discussed quite excitedly. The midwife apologised and came over with it. She said it was the most unusual placenta any of them had ever seen because it had not one, not two, but three separate issues! She showed us that the placenta was in three separate sections that were joined with membrane, and that it had been wrapped around the front, side and back of my uterus. She also said I had a "vasa previa", which is where a big vein goes across the cervix. She said that if that vein had burst then both Lily and I would have been in big trouble, and Lily was not likely to have survived. She showed us an opening in the bag that had housed Lily, and it was just millimetres away from the vein. She told us that was where my waters had broken. If that had been any closer, it would have burst the vein. She then showed us an opening just millimetres to the other side, which had been made by the surgeon's knife. Again, we had been just millimetres away from losing her. The third and final issue was that Lily's umbilical cord had been plugged into the vein, rather than the placenta, so it was a miracle she'd been able to feed properly. She was small at 6lb2, but not miniscule (even though it felt like she was when we held her for the first time!). She was our miracle baby, and I felt incredibly lucky to have her, although the trauma of what could have been stayed with me right the way through my second pregnancy and birth.

The months that followed were a heady mixture of joy and exhaustion. I was able to breastfeed and absolutely loved it. We tried introducing a bottle so that we could combination feed in order for Aaron to be more involved (and give me a bit of a break because Lily was a cluster feeder the majority of the time), but she just would not take the bottle. It was very frustrating, as those first few months were purely reliant on me being able to look after her with very little help. At four months, the pregnancy and early breastfeeding hormones were starting to wear off, and I was starting to feel my arthritis steadily getting more painful. So I started to try harder to get Lily to take a bottle, as I knew I'd soon have to stop breastfeeding in order to go back on medication. Lily, however, is incredibly stubborn, and was just not having any of it! It got to the point where I had excruciating pain in my ribs, which made picking Lily up out of her cot very difficult for me. I thought I must have pulled a muscle, so went to the GP, who referred me to urgent physio. The physio could feel inflammation and what he thought was an issue with the muscles, so he did some manipulations to try and help, but they left me in utter agony, barely able to walk home after the appointment and for a couple of days after each session. It turned out that I should have seen my rheumatologist rather than the GP, as it was the joints where my ribs join my spine that were inflamed because of the AS rather than a mechanical problem. I had to immediately stop breastfeeding to start medication to fix the issue (which was thankfully fixed very quickly), so Lily had no choice but to move on to the bottle! After that, things got a lot easier. Breastfeeding was amazing, but it was a relief to be able to pick up my baby comfortably again, as well as having Aaron able to be much more hands on.

During maternity leave, people frequently commented on motherhood "suiting" me. In truth, despite the issue with my ribs, my health had improved significantly. I was looking after myself better because I had more time to dedicate to cooking healthy food, both for me and the family. I lost the steroid weight, felt fitter and happier (the fibromyalgia in particular seems to improve the most when I am in control of my weight), and was thoroughly enjoying having more control over my health. As my maternity leave progressed, I realised I was also getting ill a lot less frequently thanks to escaping the open-plan office, as well as the stress I'd felt. All in all, I felt a lot healthier, and I was starting to worry about that changing if I went back to work.

I had many discussions with Aaron about what to do. He liked the changes in me, and didn't want me to go back to work. We worked out that if I went back full time, the majority of my wages would go on childcare, so it didn't make sense financially anyway. My mum also supported the possibility of me not going back to work, and was happy to help in any way she could. I made the decision to talk to the managing directors about my situation, and they were also very supportive. It hadn't been easy for them either, as a small business supporting a member of staff with such a high absence rate due to chronic illness, so it made life easier for them in a lot of ways too. They supported my decision to leave the company, and gave me my first freelance editing work when I decided to start my business.

September 2017, when Lily was eleven months old and ready to go to nursery a couple of days a week, I founded Fuzzy Flamingo. At first, I was doing freelance editing, alongside some design work for small businesses. I designed logos, marketing materials and more for clients, and I was enjoying it. I thought I'd wanted to move away from books, but the more design work I did outside of the publishing world, the more I missed them!

My business did well part time that first year, and I was thoroughly enjoying myself. What I had initially thought would be a bit of freelancing to keep me ticking over until Lily started school and I could get a "proper" job turned into a successful business that I was loving so much that I couldn't see me going back into traditional employment. I'd been to the London Book Fair and picked up some new publishing clients to freelance for, and was enjoying a balance between working on book production and graphic design for small businesses.

But my heart belonged to the books. I missed working directly with authors, as with the freelancing I rarely got to see how well the books were doing that I'd worked on. I developed a good relationship with the publishing houses' teams, but missed the passion you feel directly from the author. I therefore took the opportunity whilst on maternity leave at the end of 2018 and beginning of 2019 with my second daughter to refocus my marketing and go back to specialising in my first love; books. I overhauled my website, no longer offered graphic design for businesses and instead networked with authors.

My second pregnancy was even more delightful than my first because I wasn't overweight and I was fitter and healthier the second time around. I thoroughly enjoyed it! Amber also managed to hang on until the date of the c-section at thirty-nine weeks, so I got to experience how different a planned section is to an emergency one. I did, however, have a lot to worry about throughout the second pregnancy. Shortly after I discovered I was pregnant again (again I continued having periods for the first few months, but knew the signs – especially the change in my arthritis – and realised after just a few days this time), my mum was diagnosed with cancer for the third time. Although they'd thought they'd got the second lot under control, she was under palliative care, as they could only control it, not get rid of it, because the breast cancer had spread to her abdomen and surrounded multiple organs. She was still very positive, saying to me, 'I've beaten it before, I'll beat it again,' but I had a feeling she wasn't telling me the full story. The only time she let the mask of positivity drop was when I told her I was pregnant. She gave me a massive hug and said, 'Well, that gives me a reason to get through till Christmas.' When I tried to get her to elaborate, she just clammed up and said she'd been being silly! That tiny slip stayed with me.

I was mostly able to remain positive, but I kept bursting into tears at my midwife appointments. Nothing like talking about new life to get you worrying about death! The midwifery team were amazing and implemented extra appointments to keep an eye on me. But there'd be moments where I would really panic. I'd be standing in the shower and suddenly worry that I wouldn't be able to cope with a toddler and a newborn all on my own without her. At the time, my husband worked away a lot, but my mum had been there to support me the whole time. What if I didn't have that with my second baby? How would I cope?

My c-section was scheduled for the week before Christmas Day, and Amber arrived without a problem. My placenta was in three sections joined by membrane again, but thankfully that was the only issue. I do wonder if that is caused by my arthritis, or any of the medications I've been on. However, the recovery from the section was a lot harder the second time around. I was warned that recovery is harder each time, which is why they don't recommend more than three c-sections, but I didn't expect the spasms stopping me getting out of bed. They hit me like a train and I sobbed into my bedsheets as I tried to reach my alarm button to call for help as I was trapped face-down on the bed having tried to get up. It turned out that they'd got my pain meds wrong, and I'd taken nothing more than paracetamol since the birth! No wonder it hurt! They got the meds sorted and within hours I felt much better and ready to head home as a new family of four.

A week later, we were celebrating Christmas Day round my brother's house, with our gorgeous new addition. We held onto my mum tightly that year, just in case. Although she'd seemed to be doing really well, she'd had an issue with fluid on her tummy (at times joking that she looked more pregnant than I did), and again I had the feeling she wasn't telling us the full story. The fluid meant that she couldn't help me very much physically, but I was grateful for the psychological support in those first few weeks, particularly when Aaron was working away.

One day in January 2019, I called my mum and she answered sounding awful. She said she'd been throwing up and couldn't stop. The last time that happened was when the cancer had come back the second time (it was blocking her bowel) and so I told her to go to hospital. She said that the doctor had already said the same thing, so that's what she was doing. That time is all a bit of a blur and for the life of me I can't remember if she made her way into hospital herself, or if I drove her. I think it was the latter, but I wouldn't put money on it. When I saw her in hospital once she'd seen the doctor, it didn't look good. All she wanted was to go home, so I was talking to the doctors about her options. They were doing scans and trying to find out what the issue was, but they hadn't been able to stop the vomiting.

After being in the hospital a week, I got a call from the hospital asking me to go in to speak to the consultant. I was terrified because I knew that they were unlikely to be calling me in with good news. My brother was teaching and unable to come with me, but his husband and Aaron could both come, so they accompanied me to the hospital with my tiny baby in tow, while Lily was at nursery. We were taken to a side room near my mum's hospital room (she was still being sick and they'd had to rule out anything contagious first, so she had her own room at that point), but it seemed to take forever for the consultant to show up. In the end, I had to go and chase him up, as it was getting close to the time I needed to pick up Lily from nursery. When the consultant finally turned up, having been held up for several reasons, I took one look at his face and knew it wasn't good news. He told us that there was nothing more they could do for my mum except enact end of life care. I asked him how long we were talking about, and he said he couldn't say for definite but it would be a matter of weeks, not months.

It's difficult to put into words how that felt. She'd seemed to be doing so well. Other than the fluid issues on her tummy, she'd still been active, still having a giggle, still wanting to help everyone and anyone she could. To hear that we only had weeks left with her didn't seem real. I needed more time, there were so many things we'd not had the chance to do together, so many plans we'd not put into action.

She spent one more week in hospital before she managed to get herself discharged back home, where she wanted to spend her final weeks. Unfortunately, it just wasn't possible with the amount of care she needed; even with a care package in place, it just wasn't enough. When someone from LOROS, the local hospice, came round to talk to her, I was there. The one phrase that will forever stay with me was when she said, 'It is not a place people come to die. It's a place people come to live.'

And she was right. It was a wonderful place. I drove my mum there and helped her get settled into her room, then visited her every day she was there (much to her protests of, 'You've got better things to do, you've got a baby to look after.'). There were some awful times where she was really very poorly, and it was horrible to see her like that, but we also had a good laugh there and enjoyed the time we had left. She got on really well with the chap who brought the drinks trolley round, as they were trying to find her something that didn't taste awful (it was weird what happened to her tastebuds near the end).

Her final moments were spent with my brother and I holding a hand each, our husbands holding our hands, her brother and my dad with her too. Her breathing had changed, so we'd all been called in, as her death was looking imminent. It changed again while we were holding her hands, and she started to really struggle, which was distressing to see, so I squeezed her hand and said, 'Mum, just relax. Everyone is here with you, we just want you to relax, it's okay.' And with that, she seemed to visibly change, took just a few more shallower breaths and then that was it. We had to say goodbye.

CHAPTER FOURTEEN

Managing Unmanageable Stress

Since making the decision to leave full-time employment and starting my own business, I had been a lot more in control of my health. Although I still got the odd flare up, I was ill a lot less frequently, and the flare-ups happened a lot less frequently. Nothing cemented my suspicion that stress exacerbates my arthritis more than when my mum died. Towards the end of her life, I'd noticed significant hip and knee pain, but because I wanted to spend as much time with my mum as possible, I'd not talked to rheumatology about it.

My youngest was three months old, and I'd planned to finish breastfeeding at four months old to restart my medication and avoid the issues I'd experienced by leaving it too long with my eldest. But I was very glad I was still breastfeeding her when my mum was dying because it was a great form of support. Sometimes I'd just sit and feed Amber while my mum slept, and the nurses thought it was really cute that Lily, who was two at the time (there is only two years between them), would often be sitting pretending to breastfeed her dolly at the same time! Not having to worry about having the right bottles or formula during that time was a godsend, as was the release of endorphins that comes with feeding, so I am very grateful I had that at that time.

During that weird limbo time between my mum's death and her funeral, the pain in my knees and hips was getting worse. But again, I had other things to worry about, so I put off talking to rheumatology, thinking I'd call them after the funeral. But the day of the funeral, 12th of April 2019, I could barely put any weight on my left leg. My calf had suddenly got very swollen and felt hot to the touch. My mother-in-law saw it and was concerned about deep vein thrombosis, but I didn't have time or the mental capacity to think about it that day. I just had to grit my teeth and get through it.

When I woke up the following morning, it was even more hot and painful, so I called 111 and explained that I was worried it was DVT. They booked me an appointment at the walk-in clinic for that afternoon and Aaron drove me with both kids in tow. It was a Saturday, so they were understaffed and my appointment was very delayed. When I was eventually seen, the doctor measured both calves and found that my left had a 5cm bigger circumference than the right, so she was concerned about DVT too. She immediately sent me to A&E where, with hindsight, I should have just gone in the first place (I don't like to cause a fuss, though, and I can hear my brother's voice saying "you're your mother's daughter" as I write that!). If you've ever been to A&E on a Saturday, you'll know that it's full of sports injuries, particularly from football and rugby, so there was a significant wait. I eventually got seen, went through all the same questions and examination as the walk-in-centre and they also suspected DVT, but I'd need a scan to confirm it. The doctor went off to book it in and I was left in the waiting room for hours. I'd sent Aaron home with the kids because A&E isn't fun for (or with) children, but this meant that, just a day after my mum's funeral, I was dealing with the worry of DVT on my own. My dad and my best friend had both offered to keep me company, but I didn't want anyone else to have to suffer!

I was waiting so long that I ended up asking someone what had happened. I was seen by another doctor, who asked all the same questions and did the same examination. I burst into tears when it turned out I'd been caught up in the shift change and they couldn't find the notes from the first two doctors, or the scan referral! By the time they were ready to again request an ultrasound, that department was closed for the evening. I would have to return the next day to have the scan, but they couldn't send me home with a risk of DVT, so had to give me a blood thinning injection in my tummy "just in case". I was exhausted, physically and emotionally, and grateful to get into bed that night.

The next day I had to return for the ultrasound. Again, it was a long wait, but eventually the scan happened. It turned out I didn't have DVT (so needlessly had the blood thinners). My arthritis had caused a Baker's cyst on the back of my knee, which had subsequently burst and sent the fluid down my leg. They brought in a rheumatology consultant to try and help me out, who drew some of the fluid off my knee with a massive needle (ouch!) and then injected it with steroids. Within hours, I was able to put pressure on that leg, and within forty-eight hours I was walking normally again. What a relief!

This was absolute confirmation for me that stress should be avoided in order to keep more in control of my arthritis. It's not always easy, though.

I extended my leave from my business in order to give myself the time I needed to process what had happened. I accepted the offer of grief counselling from the hospice that looked after my mum in her final weeks, and I am forever grateful that I did. I am very much a "glass half full" kind of person, which serves me well most of the time, but sometimes it can lead me to avoid negative emotions. I wanted to just bury my head in the sand, pretend my mum hadn't died and avoid the grief and all the painful emotions that came with that. However, through the counselling, I knew that this wasn't a good approach and it would all come crashing down around me if I didn't face it. I hated every session, as I really don't like talking about deep emotions on the whole, and I certainly don't like crying, but it was an incredible outlet. I went from having flashbacks of my mum's worst moments, feeling like it was all too much to handle, to being able to talk about my lovely mum, remember the good times and feel like I was processing the trauma in a much healthier way.

As a result, my arthritis became much more stable

again, but I still wasn't in a place where I felt as good as when I was pregnant. The new anti-TNF I was on (Cimzia by this point, I'll explain more in the next chapter when I discuss side effects) was better than being on nothing, but it wasn't as effective as it should be. Then the whole world changed, and the control over my stress and my health felt like it was ripped away from me.

In March 2020, I was celebrating winning an award for my business, walking down a catwalk in my lingerie and feeling (mostly) great, when news of the COVID-19 pandemic started hitting the headlines more and more frequently. I had a call from my sister-in-law warning me that I shouldn't be mixing with too many people given my conditions and the medication I was on. She was right, of course, and a week later the whole country went into lockdown. This caused a few issues for me.

Firstly, I was missed off the shielding list. The GP and the rheumatologist said I should be shielding, but they blamed each other for me not getting the letter and no one would resolve it, so I had to go it alone. With no supermarket delivery slots available, and no letter to give me priority, Aaron had to do all the shopping for us, and we were really worried about him potentially bringing the virus home. The issue of me being missed off the list is still an issue nearly two years later because I still have to fight for the vaccine and look up all the new legislation myself. The GP says my coding has been changed in the system, but an AS support group I'm in shows me that I'm still not getting the correspondence I should be getting.

Secondly, I didn't qualify for any of the help for self-employed people. All the grants went off the average income over the previous three years, but I'd started my business less than three years before, had been part-time until September 2020 and had maternity and compassionate leave in there too! We thought it was only going to be a few weeks at first, so I switched to working evenings and weekends when my husband could look after the kids, and managed to get my work done. But as the weeks turned into months, the stress of no down time and no time as a family of four started to take its toll. My arthritis flared like crazy, my hair started falling out and I started to get really ill. Throw into the mix a house move, which was supposed to happen in March 2020 (we had one survey left to go when everything ground to a halt), but happened at the end of July/beginning of August with just a few weeks' notice to pack up the whole house, and the stress was far higher than I'd anticipated.

When the nurseries reopened, I was relieved. Both kids got into the nursery just a short walk from our new house, they settled in quickly, and I went full-time in my business because the new nursery was so much cheaper. The stress reduced, I found working more and having better quality time with my family much more enjoyable than ever before and it was a huge relief. I learnt a very valuable lesson: my health should be top priority, so if the nursery/school closes again I need to prioritise that over the business. My health won't take such a hard hit again, that's for sure.

CHAPTER FIFTEEN

Improving My Health to Improve My Life

Medication

I've been through a lot of different types of medication over the last decade of diagnosis, so I wanted to talk about the pros and cons of going down the medication route. I've met some people who have similar conditions to me who have been down the purely holistic route, which is amazing for them, but it's not the route I have taken. For one thing, early on I met an amazing chap in his seventies who had had AS from a young age, and he'd lost friends to AS because it can affect soft tissues like the heart without the right medication. That's also the reason I was rejected for critical illness insurance, because this disease can be fatal. That shocked me, so I asked my rheumatologist, who said that's far less likely with the medication. So, while I do things for myself outside of medication, which I will talk about in this chapter, for me I don't want to risk being unmedicated and open to critical parts of the illness like that.

The medication I started on when I was first diagnosed in Australia was various types of anti-inflammatories (also called NSAIDs), which don't do a great deal for me except taking the edge off the pain. A lot of them also come with side effects, mostly affecting the stomach, so often you have to take medication to protect the stomach whilst on these. Even with the stomach protection, I still can't take diclofenac without being confined to the bathroom a few hours a day!

I was prescribed methotrexate tablets (a type of DMARD) at the beginning too, alongside a long course of steroids to bring the initial rocket of inflammation under control. This is prescribed for my psoriatic arthritis, and it is amazing for keeping the psoriasis on my scalp (and a few other areas that flare) at bay, as well as keeping the inflammation down in my fingers and toes. However, the side effects, particularly in the beginning, were awful. It was tablets to take once a week and for the first few days each week I would feel really sick. My hair also thins and falls out with the tablets. I dealt with this for many years, but was eventually switched to methotrexate injections and they have been a game changer. I have all the benefits of the medication, but the side effects are vastly reduced for me. So it's all about trying things until I find the right balance between effective results and side effects I can cope with.

The only other DMARD I've tried is sulphasalazine. I didn't get great results from this and for me the side effects outweighed the benefits greatly. A hilarious side effect that I had been warned about before starting was that it turned my wee fluorescent! I quite enjoyed that, but maybe I have a somewhat warped sense of humour. I even turned the light out after using the toilet one day to see if it glowed in the dark because it looked like it should! It didn't, unfortunately! The only embarrassment with this was that the toilet in the old office at work didn't flush if someone had used it just before you, but luckily the rest of the female staff found it as funny as me! During this time, I got tinnitus so badly that I was struggling to hear. I was talking to someone at the NASS support group I used to attend and had to ask him to repeat what he was saying because my ears were ringing too loudly for me to catch it. He asked if I was on sulphasalazine and when I said I was it surprised me to hear that it was one of the side effects. I talked to the GP, who confirmed that was the case and took me off the tablets, and low and behold within a few days the ringing stopped. I found it very odd that taking a tablet could make your ears ring! But this reaffirmed the importance of talking about things because I would never have known it was a side effect that could be fixed.

I was fortunate to qualify for biological treatment while they were trying to get me stable when I was initially diagnosed in Australia. It is very expensive, so I was in a privileged position. They started me on Enbrel, which was an anti-TNF treatment in a weekly injection. It wasn't effective enough, so they changed me to Humira, which felt like a wonder drug for me. As you know, this stopped working when I was off it for six months after finishing my travels. Next they tried golimumab, which worked reasonably well, although not as well as the Humira did. I then came off this to try for baby number one. I went back on it in between babies one and two because by that point they had more data and had found it was safe to use up until the first stage of pregnancy. We wanted to have our two babies fairly close together in order to not have to go back on the methotrexate only to come off it six months before trying again (our daughters are two years and two months apart), the golimumab was all I could be on. It wasn't as effective the second time round, but this could have been because I didn't have anything alongside it. During this time, I was having a very strange problem. I got a lump on my bottom that was so sore and inflamed that I couldn't sit down, I had to lean and rest my weight on the side instead. I went to the GP and they diagnosed it as an infected cyst. I had to have antibiotics and wait for it to burst, which was very painful and left a horrible mark. A month later, I got another one on another part of my bottom, so the same treatment was given. I had to pause my medication every time I was on antibiotics, so that also didn't help its efficacy. This went on for a few months, with a cyst every single month. My derriere is now very scarred as a result! The GP was baffled and it got to a point where she was about to prescribe a continuous low level dose of antibiotics to stop it happening when I went into an almighty flare of my arthritis where I could hardly walk. I called the rheumatology team for help and they whisked me in to give me a steroid jab. I explained the issue with the cysts and the antibiotics and was immediately taken off the golimumab because it was a known side effect! Low and behold, without my monthly injection, the monthly cysts stopped immediately. I wasn't put on anything else at that stage because we were already trying for a baby, which the steroid jab helped with immensely! When I next saw the same rheumatology nurse and I was heavily pregnant, she claimed all credit!

After having my second baby, I was put on a new anti-TNF called Cimzia, a fortnightly injection. I was on this for almost two years and it was okay, but certainly not a wonder drug for me. I was having trouble with my back and my knees and when I needed another steroid injection into my knee joints (both at the same time, ouch!), my rheumatologist decided it was time to take me off it because it wasn't effective enough. Shortly after that discussion, and while I was waiting for my new medication to be approved, I was assigned a new GP because the one I had been seeing had retired. I'd been talking to the GP fairly regularly for about six months while we were trying to find out what on earth was going on with my menstrual cycle. Since having my youngest, I'd not had a regular period. I had spotting (like a mini period) for weeks on end, then nothing for weeks on end. I was taken off the contraceptive injection, had my hormone levels checked with blood tests and had external and internal ultrasound scans to try and find out what the issue was, but everything came back normal. The spotting was getting worse and by August it had started to happen every day with no break at all. It was very annoying! The new GP was a gynaecology specialist and we had a great chat about everything. The best thing she did was listen and be sympathetic, which I'd not had until that point. She said, 'Well, that can't be good for your relationship or your mental health!' Thank you! No, it's not, it's been pretty rubbish, and to just feel heard felt amazing. Having been through all the results and not found anything, she then went through the side effects of my medications (the list is extensive with all of them!), including the Cimzia I had just been taken off. Low and behold, one of the listed side effects was "menstrual disruption". You're telling me! This wasn't listed with the new medication, so we went ahead and she said it should be settled within a few months. That was the beginning of September and I'm happy to report at the end of December that the signs are all showing a return to a more standard cycle, phew! Again, it's highlighted that the side effects can be weird and varied! But the lesson has been learned. If I find myself with a regular and ongoing issue, check the side effects first for a quicker answer!

I am now on a new type of biological treatment, not an anti-TNF, but an IL-17 protein inhibitor called secukinumab. I started it in November 2021, and at the time of writing this section it is now New Year's Eve, so I have not been on it long. However, the virus came to call on Christmas Eve, and I was very poorly over Christmas, having to isolate alone in my bedroom because the rest of my household managed to escape it. This means that I have a delay with my medication, but hopefully only a short one! Fingers crossed this new direction in biological treatment is the right one, but if it's not then I'm not out of options.

It's all about finding what works for you.

Complementary Therapy

I've tried many different things to improve my health and well-being, so here are my top five things that help keep me healthy, happy and managing my chronic conditions well:

1. A healthy, nutritious diet. Now I don't mean the word 'diet' as in trying to lose weight, I just mean my daily intake of nutrition. I don't advocate cutting anything out unless it is harming you (for example because of allergies), but for me a healthy balanced diet works really well. I have tried many fad diets over the years to try and lose the weight I gained with the steroids, but the only thing that actually worked for me was Slimming World. I get hangry (meaning I feel angry when I'm hungry!) and so cutting calories or feeling hungry doesn't work for me. What did work was focusing on the good stuff – namely filling protein and a good balance of vegetables – and I found I ate less in general. I lost four stone in seven months, but then keeping an eighty-twenty diet of 80% on plan, 20% treats during the week meant I kept it off. I gained just over a stone during the first section of the first lockdown where I lost control of the meal planning because I couldn't do the food shop, but I am still in my healthy range and have kept to that ever since. It'll come off again when I'm ready, but the ups and downs of my medication the last couple of years means that I'm happy where I am for now! The

advantages of being at my ideal weight are that there is less pressure on my joints, the fatigue is easier to manage, and I have a lot more energy. My fibromyalgia seems to be the area most affected by weight gain, so keeping an eye on my diet means I avoid more fibro pain.

2. Moving. The worst thing I can do when my pain and stiffness increases is to stop moving. The temptation is there. When the pain levels rocket it almost seems natural to want to curl up in a little ball and stay there feeling sorry for myself. But when I do that, the pain and the stiffness gets worse, so I have to push myself to stretch, to move and to walk every single day to get better. Getting my little dog was one of the best things I ever did for this. I could no longer do the high impact exercise I used to love, such as running and aerobics, but walking was great. It's just finding the motivation to do it. So when my husband and I started looking for a fur baby in 2012, we knew we needed to find a breed that needed walking every day, but not for too long. We both worked full-time, plus I would be the one to walk him predominantly, so it needed to be an achievable target. We found that both pugs and shih-tzus needed walking for about twenty minutes minimum, which was perfect. They both had health issues as pure breeds, so we went for a cross of the two and the result was our gorgeous Doug the Shug! He gave me so much more than a reason to get out of the house and walk every

day, though. He's a hot water bottle when I'm chilly, he's a companion when I'm home alone and he's a constant source of fun, love and affection. They should put Dougs on prescription! I also have a stand-up-sit-down desk for my office, so that when I'm working I can alternate (sometimes every half hour if I'm having a particularly stiff day) between working standing up or sitting down. My smart watch also makes me get up from my desk at least once an hour to keep the blood flowing and to stretch my muscles and joints. It makes a really positive difference.

3. Rest. This seems to contradict number two, but it is all about balance and pacing myself, something I am still learning to put into practice! It is so tempting to go hell for leather when you're feeling good. To get all of those chores you've been putting off done because you're able to move more and have more energy that day and you don't know how long the good days will last. But I know from experience (and a lot of it!) that if I overdo it when I'm feeling good, I'll pay for it with a few days of extra pain and stiffness. So, whilst I may do more on the good days, it works best if I pace myself because I'll then have more good days in a row to get stuff done, rather than just the one.

4. Massage. I used to love a good massage, but ever since the painful one in Thailand, I'd not been able to find a masseuse who could help with my painful knots in

my muscles caused by overcompensating because of the inflammation in my joints without putting me into a flare for a few days. But I now have the lovely Lisa from The Serenity Shed in Leicester. She's an ex-nurse and when I met her networking I said I'd longed for a massage but could no longer have them. She promised me that if she gave me a massage that put me into flare, she'd give me my money back. And now I have one every month with her, she's amazing! So whilst I'd advocate for the benefits of a good massage in supporting the muscles that in turn support the joints, do your research and find someone who knows about your conditions and what to avoid, otherwise it's pretty pointless! I've also had good experiences with acupuncture, which feels very weird at first!

5. Personal development. I'd not done this before having my own business, so it felt very alien at first. When you get into the world of networking and business it is all over the place, but outside of that it's not really talked about as much. But it has been very valuable. Personal development is working on yourself, predominantly your mindset, in order to grow. Personally, I think it should be taught in schools. Through personal development, I have been able to shift my mindset (mind over matter is very powerful), find mindfulness and learn to prioritise myself in order to help those closest to me. The phrase from airline cabin crew of "put your own gas mask on first before helping others"

speaks volumes to me. My natural instinct is to prioritise my family and friends, with me much lower down the list. However, when I do this, my health suffers both physically and mentally, and then I'm no use to anyone, my family, friends or myself. Just look what happened when I did that during the first lockdown! So now I work on myself, give myself time and space, and everyone around me feels the benefit.

Mindset

It can be a bit of a minefield out there when you look into improving your mindset, as there are so many people talking about different things to help, with some claiming they have the keys to this complex field. I would advise taking it gently, reading what takes your fancy and working through it at your own pace. Small steps will make a huge difference in the long run, but if you try and learn everything you can too quickly it can be overwhelming. Little regular changes will really help. There can also be a bit of an issue with 'toxic positivity', where you feel like in order to change your mindset you have to be positive all the time, and there's no room for any negativity at all. However, you are human. You will feel negative emotions, you will feel down, and that is absolutely okay. The key for me (thanks to coaching as well as the amazing grief counselling I received from LOROS hospice after my mum died) is to acknowledge these feelings, allow myself to feel them and then use my tools to move past them. I now like to think of it like this:

> I may still seek the silver linings, but it doesn't
> mean I don't see the rain.

For me there are two main things that have really improved for my mindset: setting goals and flipping the script. I never set goals before having my own business, but now I do it for both my business and my personal life and it really works for me. At the beginning of the year (which just happened to be when I started, you can start at any point, don't wait for "a good time" or it'll never come) I set three business goals and three personal goals. I then break those down into what I want to achieve per quarter of a year to get closer to achieving those, then break that further into weekly chunks. If I do things little and often then it is manageable, and I am more likely to succeed. For example, one of my business goals this year is to publish my own book (which overlaps into personal goals too), which will give me more empathy with my authors having been through the whole process myself. One of my personal goals is to raise money for charity. I'm on my way to achieving both because I put manageable steps into place. I don't set specific goals for my arthritis, but I do have health related goals regularly, such as managing my weight and how active I am, which in turn helps me get healthier and more able to manage it. Having things to look forward to and work towards also really helps me mentally, so I always pop in some fun goals to work towards!

Flipping the script has been a lot harder, and I am still working on that, but I've made great progress. I am naturally a pretty positive person, but sometimes I can feel overwhelmed with how poorly I can feel, and the worry about what might happen in the future. For example, nearer the beginning of the diagnosis I worried that Aaron may feel trapped into staying with me because of it, and/ or that I would become a burden to him. However, by flipping the script and thinking about the positives, I think about the negatives a lot less, and they can even seem less significant. For example, I talk myself through thoughts like this by imagining someone else was sharing their worries: if someone told me they were worried their other half was only with them because of their illness, I would tell them that they are their own person and wouldn't be with them unless they loved them. Aaron is a big boy, he can make his own decisions and I know in my heart he is with me because he wants to be! I am also a big fan of gratitude (my mum used to call it counting your blessings) and this helps me feel good. In the darkest times it can be really hard to think of anything positive, but the more you practise the easier it becomes. Start with the small things and the bigger things will come. Small things for me are that I am still able to walk my dog, even on the worst pain days, even if that's the only walking I'm able to do that day. Bigger things are that I may not have gone down the self-employment route were it not for my arthritis, and I will forever be grateful for that. My mum said after the realisation of how close we came to losing Lily at birth that this may be the reason

I have arthritis – to save her life by needing a c-section and bringing her wonderful soul into the world. It's a lovely way to look at it.

Flipping the script has especially helped me during the tough times. I have a blue badge for when the going gets really tough; I filled in the forms and also had a face-to-face assessment, so I know that I am entitled to it, but for a while I didn't feel like I deserved it. I would be embarrassed and feared the looks and the comments that I have often received when using it, as I don't "look" disabled. However, I now realise that this is their issue not mine. They don't know how much it hurts sometimes when I'm struggling to put one foot in front of the other. But the need to make a negative comment comes from their negativity, not mine, so I feel much more comfortable using the tools I have to improve my life now, regardless of what others think. There may well be a time soon when I need a stick to help me walk, as I relied on using the pushchair as a walking aid but my youngest no longer needs it! I have really worried about this, about how it would look and feel to have something so visible signifying my often-invisible illness. So, I have a plan! When I invest in a stick, I am going to invest in a gorgeous one and make a statement, something I would be proud to use. I have my eye on a Neo Walkstick (they're so pretty!): https://www.neo-walk.com/

There are so many ways to support yourself when you have a chronic illness. Personally, I have distanced myself from all except one online AS support group (they give very valuable information and are supported by the charity NASS) because the negativity from most groups brings me down. I know it isn't a good thing to have a chronic illness, but seeing posts every day talking about how awful it is doesn't help me. The posts I want to see are about ways I can improve my health, tips on dealing with the bad days and information about new treatments available. I'm not saying that you shouldn't have a whinge sometimes, as we all need to vent and we shouldn't bottle things up. But when that's happening every day then what I'm suggesting is that we flip the script and find solutions and ways to make positive change. There may not be a cure, there may not be anything we can do to instantly feel better, but there are small changes we can make each day to set us on a more positive path to feeling good more than we feel bad. And that's all any of us really wants, isn't it?

Conclusion

Since my diagnosis in 2009, there have been some pretty major lows, but there have also been highs and everything in between. I've learned a lot about my conditions and also about myself, so here's what I'd like you to take away from this book.

Life is all about balance. One of the things I've learned through my personal development is that I don't respond well to people who are super-duper positive all the time, or people who are totally down and negative all the time. Instead, I respond well to people who keep it real, talk about the bad stuff, but also talk about the good stuff, particularly if they help you find how you can have more good than bad! If things aren't going too well, try and make a shift to bring more of the good stuff in. Yes, do vent when you're having a bad day, have a cry, shout about how unfair it feels sometimes, but try not to stay in that place and wallow. It can feel really lonely sometimes, but reach out to someone when you're feeling low. Ask for help. Sometimes even the people closest to us have no idea what we're going through, so talk it out, say how you feel, and make a plan for how to move forward. I am lucky to be surrounded by amazing people who keep me going, including a lot of coaches, some of whom I work with personally. One of my favourite places to be is in the company of Holly Matthews, who runs The Happy Me Project. She has many tools to help you to feel (in her words) "less crappy and more happy". Check out her website: https://www.iamhollymatthews. com/thehappymeproject/ for more details. I also love working with my business coach (she's a business and life coach hybrid) Kerry Hearsey, who has worked wonders on my personal life as well as my business (https://www. kerryhearsey.com/). Kerry also has a fab podcast about confidence, which she hosts with another awesome coach Adam Hulme (https://www.kerryhearsey.com/podcast). Confidence can be a very powerful tool when you have a chronic illness, as it helps with all aspects of it, from feeling confident enough to ask for help (I know I've suffered with pride preventing me doing so in the past) to feeling confident walking down the street with that walking aid if you need one.

Everything happens for a reason. My mum used to say this a lot, and the older I get, the more it rings true. I even named my chapter this in a book I collaborated on called *Meanings Over Milestones* by the Positive Motherhood Project (https://www.meaningsovermilestones.com/). There are positive things that have happened to me as a result of my diagnosis. Without it, I may well have taken the path of a career in the police. As I have got older, I now see that it was not a path I was likely to have enjoyed. Instead, I found a new passion for books and enjoyed a wonderful career in the publishing industry. It also gave me the push I needed to start my own business, which has now won multiple awards and fills me with joy. And not to mention having my two wonderful girls! Finding things to be grateful for can be a really powerful tool to leading a happy and fulfilled life, and boy do I have a lot to be grateful for!

It's not always easy, but that's okay. There will be tough days where I wonder how I'm going to continue, where I need help with everything from looking after the kids to putting my own socks on. But those days pass, and there are also days with sunshine and rainbows to follow, even if it's hard to see it in the depths of a horrible flare. I've talked about the tough times on a number of platforms, from being a guest speaker to writing chapters in collaboration books to writing blog posts. The one that sums up what I find most difficult is the one I wrote for the 'Just One Mama' blog about dealing with mum guilt. It is the thing that I find hardest to deal with, but I'm getting there. Have a read here: https://www.justonemama.co.uk/post/fighting-mum-guilt-with-a-chronic-illness and know that however you're feeling, that's okay. We all feel a range of emotions day-to-day, it's not possible to be positive all the time, but it is possible to make positive steps to finding more happiness.

Acknowledgements

Thank you so much to everyone who has supported me over the years, and to all of you for reading this book. If you've enjoyed it, please do leave me a review on Amazon, as they help immensely with getting books seen by more people. And if you know anyone with a chronic illness, who may just find this book interesting or helpful, please do tell them about it!

Travelling is in my blood. I'd like to first thank Aunty Phyll and great-uncle George for initially sparking my desire to travel thanks to their tales of Chinese food and dresses in Hong Kong, their millennium spent in the pool at Tom and Kim's house in Australia, and Aunty Phyll's cooking, especially her Thai green curry and Greek tzatziki.

Thanks also to Uncle Ian (aka Gruncle) and Manuela for your infamous slide shows of your travels, especially Australia and the US. The combined stories and photos inspired me to want to travel.

Thank you to Aaron. Your support from the moment you stuck by me in Australia, to helping me on my way with Fuzzy Flamingo means the world to me.

To my family. My mum and dad, as well as Aaron's

mum and dad for keeping us making memories when we were on the brink of giving up our travels. To Mark and Mark, for being there in the good times and the bad. You all make me very happy.

A huge thank you needs to go to those people who helped this book come to life. My beta readers gave me fantastic feedback and helped get the early draft in far better shape, so thank you to Gail Brown, Dawn Chivers, Lucy Georgiades and Laura Southorn. And thank you to Steven Smith (author of the fantastic *Chasing Shadows* – go check it out – and one of my freelance proofreaders) for doing a great job with the final proofread. Thanks also go to Sarah Taylor for her fantastic help and advice on the marketing front. Everyone's help has been very much appreciated and helped ease the nerves of publishing my first full solo book!

Finally, thank you to the National Axial Spondyloarthritis Society (NASS) for supporting me and many others like me living with AS. They are a brilliant source of information and really helpful if ever you need a helping hand when it comes to living with this condition. They have been really supportive of my book, and helping me to help others, so as a thank you I am donating £1 from every paperback sale to them. And this circles back to you, dear reader. In purchasing this paperback, you have donated to a wonderful charity, so thank you.

Contact Me

Whether you'd like to talk about this book, you'd like to chat about chronic illness, have a press enquiry or you'd like help publishing your own book, I'd love to hear from you. You can get in touch in a number of ways:

Website:
www.fuzzyflamingo.co.uk

Email:
contact@fuzzyflamingo.co.uk

Facebook:
https://www.facebook.com/FuzzyFlamingoDesign/

Instagram:
https://www.instagram.com/fuzzyflamingodesign/

LinkedIn:
https://www.linkedin.com/in/jen-parker-fuzzy-flamingo/

Twitter:
https://twitter.com/FlamingoFuzzy

If you love books, whether you're a reader or a writer, come and join my flamazing community of people sharing their passion:
https://www.facebook.com/groups/
fuzzyflamingobooklovers

About the National Axial Spondyloarthritis Society (NASS)

NASS

Axial SpA
works silently.
We don't.

At NASS, we transform the diagnosis and care of people living with axial SpA. It's an invisible and misdiagnosed condition. Often leaving people feeling powerless, in increasing pain and extreme exhaustion. We campaign policy makers for early diagnosis and better services. We work with the NHS to get axial SpA identified and diagnosed quickly. We're determined that everyone receives effective care. We make sure people with axial SpA get the latest information and the support they need to tackle living with the condition. And we build an active community, online and through our local branches across the UK. We are with them all the way. Axial SpA works silently. We don't.